MICROSCOPE

KEITH

W9-ABI-432

WITHDRAWN
L. R. COLLEGE LIBRARY

Animal and Plant Diversity

PRENTICE-HALL

FOUNDATIONS OF BIOLOGY PROGRAM

William D. McElroy and Carl P. Swanson, *Editors*

ABOUT THIS PROGRAM

A few years ago the series editors of this biology program were involved in the preparation of a college-level series entitled *Foundations of Modern Biology*. Although the volumes had been written for the college student, a number of them found their way into high school classrooms. Since that time, extensive inquiry among teachers of high school biology have indicated that a similar program, more limited in scope and oriented specifically to high school students, would fill a real need. With that encouragement, we have planned the present FOUNDATIONS OF BIOLOGY PROGRAM.

Realizing that the subject matter and philosophy of biology are an extremely important part of the liberal education of every citizen, we felt that a biology program should be varied, yet pertinent. It should also do the following: 1. convey something of the meaning, scope, and excitement of biological science as a significant perspective from which to view the world; 2. provide an acquaintance with the world of living things, and of the relationships of one organism to others; 3. provide a knowledge of the structure and function of organisms and of populations; and 4. provide a knowledge of man: his history as an organism, his relation to other organisms, his rise to a position of dominance in the biological world, and the ways in which he functions as an animal and as a human being. In general, these are our goals in the four parts comprising this program.

The FOUNDATIONS OF BIOLOGY PROGRAM also includes a separate volume, *Investigations of Cells and Organisms: A Laboratory Study in Biology* by Dr. Peter Abramoff and Dr. Robert Thomson.

All of us—authors and editors alike—are grateful for the excellent advice and constructive criticism so generously offered by the many high school teachers and college teachers who helped in the preparation of this program. Their familiarity with the level, comprehension, and needs of high school students has been extremely valuable to us. Those who have been particularly helpful, and who deserve our particular thanks, are EDWIN M. FIELDS, Assistant Principal, Fairview High School, Boulder, Colorado; CAROL L. CROW, El Cerrito High School, El Cerrito, California; VINCENT J. SILLUZIO, Newton South High School, Newton Centre, Massachusetts; DR. ELIZABETH A. SIMENDINGER, The Wheatley School, Old Westbury, Long Island, New York; DR. IRWIN SPEAR, University of Texas; DR. R. W. VAN NORMAN, University of Utah.

—*The Editors*

Animal and

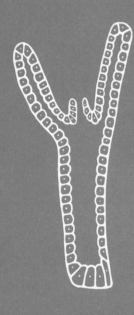

PART 1

FOUNDATIONS OF BIOLOGY PROGRAM

William D. McElroy and Carl P. Swanson, *Editors*

Roy A. Gallant, *Editorial Adviser*

Prentice-Hall, Inc., *Englewood Cliffs, New Jersey*

Plant Diversity

Neal D. Buffaloe

CARL A. RUDISILL LIBRARY
LENOIR-RHYNE COLLEGE

Photograph: Dennis Brokaw,
From National Audobon Society.

ABOUT THE COVER

To perceive nature with the photographer's eye is to stretch the sense of vision to its limits. Dennis Brokaw, who took this spectacular photograph of a southern California grass spider described his picture in these words: "No amount of skill and expertise in the handling of flashlamps can produce the photograph made by existing light, for it is in that light only that we live and perceive."

FOUNDATIONS OF BIOLOGY PROGRAM
William D. McElroy and Carl P. Swanson, Editors

ANIMAL AND PLANT DIVERSITY
Neal D. Buffaloe

© 1968 by PRENTICE-HALL, INC.
Englewood Cliffs, New Jersey
All rights reserved. No part of this book
may be reproduced in any form or by any means
without permission in writing from the publisher.

Current printing (last digit):
10 9 8 7 6 5 4 3 2

Library of Congress Catalog Card Number: 68-10006
Printed in the United States of America

Designer   Merrill Haber

Illustrations   Prepared by Joseph M. Sedacca,
Robert Bryant, Juan Barberis,
scientific illustration specialists who are
also employed as graphic designers at
The American Museum of Natural History,
New York, N.Y.

Picture Research   Gabriele Wunderlich

CARL A. RUDISILL LIBRARY
LENOIR-RHYNE COLLEGE

ABOUT THIS BOOK

Have you ever encountered some plant or animal totally unknown to you? Chances are that you have, and if you are like many people, when you see an unusual organism your curiosity is aroused.

Biologists are concerned with the study of organisms at many different levels of organization. In fact, there are so many ways in which life can be studied that biology is a very broad field. For example, if you are enrolled in a biology course that continues throughout the school year, you will have studied such diverse topics as cells, molecules, energy transformations, and populations of animals. Nevertheless, these and other aspects of biology ultimately relate to individual organisms, and to a great extent they may appear meaningless unless they are so related.

The author holds the view that the first responsibility of a high school biology teacher is to stimulate interest in and appreciation for organisms in nature. There will be time later to explore other and more detailed viewpoints, such as cytology and biochemistry. For a student to have participated in a biology course during the whole of an academic year and *still* walk among the sights and sounds of nature ignorantly is nothing short of tragic.

This book is not a catalog of either common or unusual organisms. Rather, it is a presentation of basic *groups* of organisms. It is also concerned with the principles that guide biologists in their study of living forms. The aim of the book is that of providing a basis for understanding plant and animal diversity in its broader aspects. Once you have learned the fundamental concepts, you will find it much easier to identify individual organisms and to relate them to the larger world of life.

The author wishes to acknowledge with gratitude the assistance and criticisms of many colleagues. He wishes especially to thank Professors Harold C. Bold, Richard A. Collins, Robert T. Kirkwood, and Jewel E. Moore for their considerable help. It is always a pleasure to work with the staff of Prentice-Hall, and the other authors of this series have been most helpful. Finally, he wishes to express appreciation to the many biologists who have been concerned in recent years with the definition of standards in the teaching of high school biology.

—Neal D. Buffaloe

Conway, Arkansas

CONTENTS

Animal and Plant Diversity

1 THE DIVERSITY OF LIVING THINGS

Esther Bubley

Man's environment consists of a great many kinds of things. There are inanimate objects, both natural and man made, and the various manifestations of energy that surround us, such as light, heat, and radio waves. Most of us are in close contact with other people and, indirectly, we meet them through their ideas when we read or watch television. Furthermore, other living forms figure prominently in our environment (Fig. 1.1).

A great many fields of learning help us to know and understand our environment, and, of course, such knowledge and understanding are very important to us. After all, we are going to encounter objects, forms of energy, people, and various plants and animals as long as we live. Regardless of a person's present and future activities in his society, a knowledge and an understanding of his surroundings will do much to equip him for living successfully in that society.

Fig. 1.1 A contrast in human environments. What advantages can we assume the country environment to have over the city-street environment? What are some of the biological problems faced by the astronaut in the closed ecological environment?

N.A.S.A.

In this book, we are going to examine some of the living things which are part of our environment. In considering these, you will be amazed by the seemingly limitless **diversity,** or variety, of animals and plants. If you were not already familiar with many different kinds of plants and animals, you would marvel at the wonderful variety which nature has produced. Suppose that a person who is almost totally unfamiliar with wildlife decides to spend one hour in a wooded area, one hour in a grassy field, and an hour beside a pond. It is a spring day and the plants and animals in these areas are typical, both in number and variety. If he looks closely, this person will see hundreds of different kinds of living things, or **organisms.** If he makes several sweeps with an insect net in the grassy field, he will find an even greater number; and by drawing a finely-woven net through the pond water, hundreds more organisms would be revealed. Many of them would be microscopic in size, as would many others found on debris from the field and wood.

Over the hundreds of years biologists have been collecting and studying plants and animals, they have catalogued well over 1,000,000 different kinds of animals, and about 350,000 different kinds of plants. Yet there are many more plant and animal types that remain to be described. An average of about 10,000 new animals and 5,000 new plants are described each year by biologists.

With such an array, it is small wonder that we find great diversity among animals and among plants. What is the largest living thing you can think of? (The largest living thing is not an animal, but a plant.) The Blue Whale, which is bigger than any other modern animal (about 100 feet long) is 10,000,000 times as long as the smallest living animal, which is one life stage of a certain tiny parasite called a microsporidian. As Fig. 1.2 shows, there is an even greater contrast in size between the largest and the smallest plants. Diversity occurs not only in size, but in shape, structure, function, life span, and reproduction. On the microscopic level, differences in tissues and cells can mark one kind of organism from another. At the molecular level, small differences in structure produce major differences at higher levels.

The general field of biology includes many subfields, each giving us a special way of looking at living things. The subfield of **taxonomy** is concerned with the classification of organisms according to their differences and similarities. **Ecology,** a much younger science, is the study of an organism's relationships to its environment. To the taxonomist, diversity and similarity among animals, or among plants, enable him to place certain organisms together in one group or to assign them to different

Fig. 1.2 Comparative sizes and shapes of selected plants and animals. The sizes given represent either typical or maximum measurements through the longest axis of the plant or animal body. As an exercise, compute the height of a sequoia tree if it were magnified as highly as the bacterium shown here.

groups. For example, all animals that have hair, secrete milk, and have certain other things in common are placed in a group called **Mammalia.**

The ecologist is interested in those features and habits of an animal or plant that enable it to survive in a given environment. For example, over the past 25 years more than half of the sheep in an area of Australia called Pilbara have died out. Meanwhile, kangaroos in the area have flourished. An ecologist who studied this area discovered that over the years the sheep gradually depleted the choice food plants. This permitted spiky grass called *spinifex*, which is a poor food for sheep, to spread. With only spinifex as their major diet, the adult female sheep could not produce enough milk to keep their lambs alive. The kangaroos, however, thrived on spinifex and increased in number. By studying the plants, animals, and other elements making up a given environment, and by understanding how they act on each other, the ecologist adds a new dimension to the study of natural history. In the chapters that follow, we shall deal with the diversity of living things from the taxonomist's view and from the view of the ecologist.

FOR THOUGHT AND DISCUSSION

1 Make a list of 15 different animals, writing down their names as quickly as you can think of them. Time yourself, and record the time that it took you. Now repeat the exercise for 15 different plants. Which list took you longer to compile? If there was a marked difference in the time required, how do you account for it?

2 Three biologists are asked to make a survey of a certain small desert. Of the three, one is a plant taxonomist, another is an animal taxonomist, and the third is an ecologist. Their only instructions are to "study the area." In general terms, how do you think each person should proceed?

3 If your library has the first and third books listed below, read the first chapter of either (or both if time permits). Make a list of new concepts that you gain about science and biology.

SELECTED READINGS

Buffaloe and Throneberry *Principles of Biology.* (2nd ed.) Englewood Cliffs, N.J.: Prentice-Hall, Inc. (in press).

Froman, Robert. *Wanted: Amateur Scientists.* New York: McKay Publishing Co., 1963.
   This is an excellent, short book in which the author discusses opportunities for the amateur scientist and his important role in modern research. It is of particular value to the beginning student of the natural sciences.

Weisz, P. B. *The Science of Biology* (2nd. ed.). New York: McGraw-Hill Book Co., Inc., 1963.

2 HOW ANIMALS AND PLANTS ARE CLASSIFIED

In Chapter 1, our discussion of plant and animal diversity was quite general. We spoke of different "kinds" of organisms, but we did not give "kind" a specific meaning. This term is too vague to be of much use in biology, although it does tell us that the organisms to which we refer are alike in some way. Instead of "kind," biologists say **species** (Fig. 2.1). How much alike do organisms have to be in order to qualify as a species? In what ways do domesticated cats differ from wildcats? How do wild dogs differ from wolves? Before such questions as these can be considered meaningfully, it is necessary to find out how, over the years, scientists have come to classify living things.

Fig. 2.1 Giraffes and zebras shown grazing in their native Rhodesia. Although these two animals have many similar characteristics, they are obviously different enough to be regarded as separate kinds, or species. Without knowing any more about giraffes and zebras than you can learn by studying this photograph, can you list three differences between them?

Courtesy of The American Museum of Natural History

Old Systems of Classification

From ancient writings we learn that men have long recognized a fundamental difference between plants and animals and placed organisms in one of two great *kingdoms*. The Greek philosopher Aristotle (384–322 B.C.) seems to have been the first person to attempt to devise a detailed classification of organisms. He worked chiefly with animals and classified several hundred varieties. Although it is more accurate to describe Aristotle's attempts at classification as a listing rather than a system, it was a beginning, nevertheless. In addition, he inspired one of his students, Theophrastus, to make a similar study of plants.

From the time of Aristotle until the 1700's, there was remarkably little improvement over the "lists" drawn up by the Greek scholar. Even the better attempts to classify living things were not very successful, partly because communication between naturalists was so poor. It was not until the middle of the 18th Century that a truly excellent system was devised, and it was due to the genius and persistence of its inventor that it became widely accepted. This man was Karl von Linné (1707–78), a Swedish botanist who is better known by the name Carolus Linnaeus.

Building on the work of others to a certain extent, Linnaeus devised such a workable system that taxonomists still use it today. There are two main principles of this system: 1. the use of Latin, or Latinized, words to name groups of organisms; and 2. the use of categories that rank organisms from broad groupings to narrow groupings. Linnaeus used Latin because it was the language of scholarship in his day, and since it still serves us quite well, the practice continues. The categories that Linnaeus defined were **kingdom, class, order, genus** (plural **genera**), and **species** (plural **species**). Organisms can be ranked in these categories in such a way that a kingdom consists of many classes, a class includes several orders, an order includes several genera, a genus includes several species, and a species consists of relatively closely related organisms.

Such a system of categories was not new; others had used these and other categories in various schemes. The real genius of Linnaeus lay in his ability to rank organisms and groups of organisms in a **natural** order. Up to this time, systems had been largely **artificial.** For example, most taxonomists before Linnaeus had classified whales, dolphins, and other aquatic mammals with the fishes, simply because of their superficial resemblance to each other. Linnaeus, however, recognized that these aquatic mammals were much more similar to the land mammals than to the fishes, and he classified them accordingly. We now interpret similarities and differences among organisms as indicating close or distant evolutionary kinship, which Linnaeus did not, but his ranking of plants and animals according to really significant traits was a step in the right direction.

Another extremely important principle that Linnaeus introduced into taxonomy was the use of a single word for the specific name. Hence, the generic and specific names of an organism became a useful and convenient **binomial** (meaning *two-name*), much like your first and last names. All human beings are classified *Homo sapiens. Homo* is the generic name; *sapiens* is the specific name. This highly efficient system made it possible for the first time to classify new organisms and rename the old ones in a consistent way. Linnaeus is remembered best today for his emphasis on the generic-specific names. His system is called **binomial nomenclature** ("naming with two names").

Here is an example of how this system works. Linnaeus placed all oak trees in the genus *Quercus* (which is the Latin word for oak). There are several species of oak trees, a few of which are *Quercus alba,* white oak, *Quercus rubrum,* red oak, *Quercus nigra,* water oak, and *Quercus phellos,* willow oak. These names, as well as hundreds of others given by Linnaeus, are still used today.

Modern Taxonomy and the Species Problem

Because Linnaeus was unable to predict the vast number of new plants and animals to be discovered and classified, taxonomists have had to create additional categories. Today, the major categories are kingdom, **phylum,** class, order, **family,** genus, and species. Two major groups—phylum and family—have been added to the five of Linnaeus. Furthermore, it sometimes becomes necessary to add still other categories, such as subphylum, subclass, group, tribe, and so on.

Here is an example of how the Linnaean system is used today. Starting from the most general category (kingdom) and working our way to the most specific category (species), let us classify the domestic dog. We begin by grouping the dog in the animal kingdom, or as it is expressed in Latinized form, the kingdom **Animalia.** The animal kingdom includes several phyla (plural of phylum). One of them is the phylum **Chordata,** made up of all animals that have a **notochord** at some stage of their development. Similar to a backbone, the notochord is a supporting rod-like structure that runs the length of the animal just beneath the **dorsal** (upper) body surface. There are other characteristics of this phylum, and since the dog fits them all, it is included. See Fig. 2.2.

At this point in our classification, we must include a subphylum

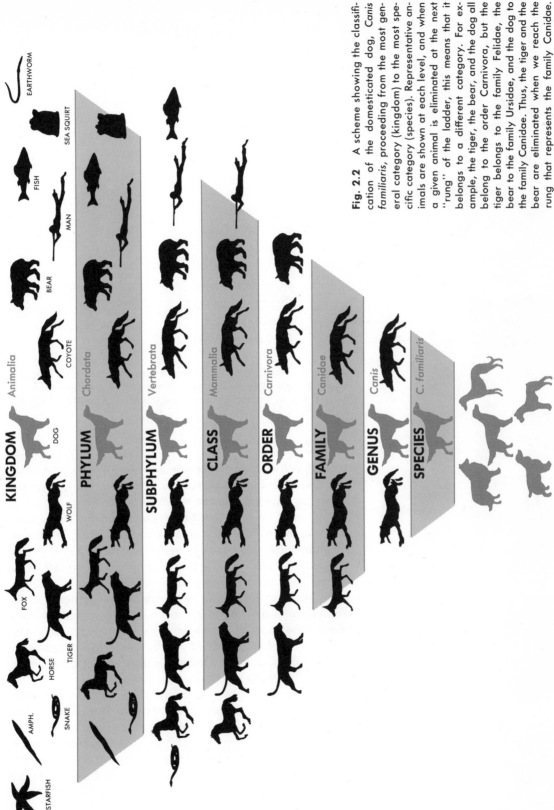

Fig. 2.2 A scheme showing the classification of the domesticated dog, *Canis familiaris*, proceeding from the most general category (kingdom) to the most specific category (species). Representative animals are shown at each level, and when a given animal is eliminated at the next "rung" of the ladder, this means that it belongs to a different category. For example, the tiger, the bear, and the dog all belong to the order Carnivora, but the tiger belongs to the family Felidae, the bear to the family Ursidae, and the dog to the family Canidae. Thus, the tiger and the bear are eliminated when we reach the rung that represents the family Canidae.

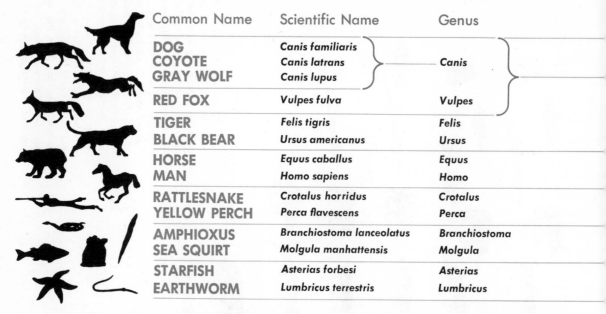

Common Name	Scientific Name	Genus
DOG	*Canis familiaris*	
COYOTE	*Canis latrans*	*Canis*
GRAY WOLF	*Canis lupus*	
RED FOX	*Vulpes fulva*	*Vulpes*
TIGER	*Felis tigris*	*Felis*
BLACK BEAR	*Ursus americanus*	*Ursus*
HORSE	*Equus caballus*	*Equus*
MAN	*Homo sapiens*	*Homo*
RATTLESNAKE	*Crotalus horridus*	*Crotalus*
YELLOW PERCH	*Perca flavescens*	*Perca*
AMPHIOXUS	*Branchiostoma lanceolatus*	*Branchiostoma*
SEA SQUIRT	*Molgula manhattensis*	*Molgula*
STARFISH	*Asterias forbesi*	*Asterias*
EARTHWORM	*Lumbricus terrestris*	*Lumbricus*

Fig. 2.3 A scheme to show the inclusive nature of taxonomic categories, using the animals shown in figure 2.2. These animals are merely examples, of course, and do not represent a broad sampling of the animal kingdom.

to single out those chordates whose notochord is replaced by a vertebral column, or backbone, during embryonic development. Since the dog is a **vertebrate** (an animal with a vertebral column), it is included in the subphylum **Vertebrata.** There are many classes of vertebrates. One class includes all those vertebrates which produce milk to suckle their young. This is the class **Mammalia,** and our dog qualifies for this group.

It is easy to see what is happening as we proceed in this manner. Each time we move down one rung on the classification ladder we exclude a vast number of animals. At the mammal stage, however, there are still many different kinds of animals that meet the requirements met by our dog. How many other such animals can you think of? What we must do now is continue down the ladder until we reach the rung that excludes all animals except the dog.

One of the many orders of mammals is the order **Carnivora.** It includes the natural meat eaters, and the dog is one of these, along with the various cats, bears, weasels, and so on. As we move the dog down into the family grouping **Canidae,** we exclude all animals except the dog, foxes, wolves, and coyotes. The genus **Canis** includes just the dogs, wolves, and coyotes. Finally we move the dog down to the species level, **familiaris,** where it,

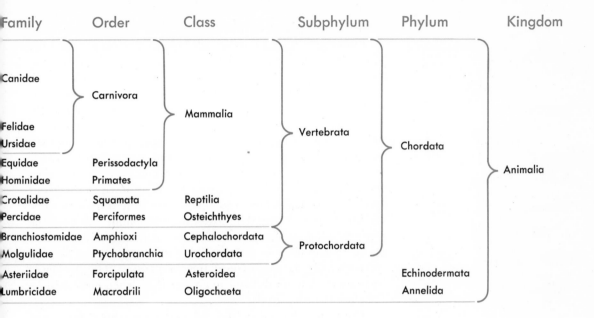

and it alone, is included. See Fig. 2.3.

It is easy to see, by this scheme, that a given category can be defined as a group of lesser categories, at least until we reach the species. A class is a group of similar orders; an order is a group of similar families, and so on. But we still have the same old problem—what do we mean by "similar?" Although we went a certain way in defining the word by showing similarities between the common dog and other animals, taxonomists need more technical definitions. Often it is necessary for them to make a final decision that is based on the judgment of one or more taxonomists. Consequently, not all botanists and zoologists are in complete agreement about the various groups that should be set up in an ideal classification of the plant and animal kingdoms—and they probably never will be.

The ideal is a completely natural system, arranged in the manner in which organisms evolved. However, the problem here is that the evidence is too fragmentary to allow for certainty in most cases. This means, in the final analysis, that taxonomic systems are natural only to a limited extent.

As we have pointed out, Linnaeus strove for a "natural" system, even though he did not view plant and animal diversity in the same light that we do today. A natural classification to a modern taxonomist is one that follows evolutionary lines. To Linnaeus it meant kinship in a figurative sense, in much the same way that we would say two automobiles are "kin" because they represent two lines produced by the same manufacturer. In spite of this difference in viewpoint, his classification of plants and animals was surprisingly "natural" by modern standards.

We have already mentioned the taxonomic problem of defining degrees of similarity. For example, just how "similar" do genera have to be in order to comprise a family? Dogs, foxes, wolves, and coyotes are similar enough to be placed in the same family, but when we move them down to the genus level, only dogs, wolves, and coyotes are similar enough to be included under *Canis*. The foxes are left behind. We have the same problem at the species level, but it is intensified because on the species level we are describing *real organisms,* not abstract categories. On the species level, the old question "How similar?" becomes even more difficult to answer than when it is asked on the class or order levels.

The fact is that no satisfactory and acceptable definition of the species as a taxonomic grouping has yet been formulated. However, there are some general and reliable rules that we can follow. Close similarity in appearance is one that is usually dependable, although one must know what similarities to look for. So far in our discussion we have mentioned only those similarities that can be determined by the naked eye. This was a necessary and good first step, but as our knowledge of living things has grown over the years as a result of improved techniques of studying organisms, we can now look for similarities and differences on the microscopic level as well.

At the cellular level, members of the same species have **chromosomes** that are usually the same in number and form. Chromosomes are structures located in the central part of a cell. They are carriers of **genes,** or determiners of hereditary traits such as height, eye color, and so on. We shall have more to say about chromosomes later. At the molecular level, the internal chemical activities of members of the same species is generally very similar. Consequently, a species is, at the very least, a group of organisms that are similar in appearance, have the same number and form of chromosomes, and have similar body chemistry.

However, this is hardly enough. Some organisms are indistinguishable from each other on this basis. They look alike, they have the same number and form of chromosomes, and their body chemistry is the same; yet, they cannot be made to interbreed. For example, some species of katydids are so much alike that they can be readily distinguished only by listening to their song patterns. In spite of their close similarities according to the criteria listed above, they do not interbreed. Sexual compatability, or interbreeding, is one of the best ways of judging the "similarity" of organisms, although it is not absolutely reliable. Some species that are not similar, according to the rules just mentioned, interbreed successfully. The horse and the donkey are one example. We can refine our rule about sexual compatability somewhat by saying that a species may be considered a group of organisms which interbreed freely in nature and which produce offspring that are capable of further successful interbreeding with each other.

The major trouble with determining the exact limits of a species is the fact that its members are not static, but changing. For example, a fairly common phenomenon in nature is the geographical separation of two populations of the same species. (See Darwin's finches on page 24.) Each undergoes basic changes on the cell level, and after a few decades, centuries, or millenia, there are two groups that may look alike but whose reproductive cells are quite different as regards their internal content. Let us assume that the geographical barrier which separated them initially is removed, say, a broad river that changed its course. They are brought back together, but interbreeding does not produce offspring. By our definition, we now have two species. Had we brought them together earlier they might have interbred but produced infertile offspring. Or they might have produced fewer offspring than before. At such times taxonomists apply the term **subspecies** to one or the other of the groups. The problem is an enormous one. The point is, however, that evolution (change) makes it impossible to define a species in hard-and-fast terms. See Fig. 2.4.

The general principles laid down by Linnaeus have served us very well over the years. The fact that more than a million species of plants and animals have been named and classified according to his system in the two centuries following Linnaeus is testimony to the value of his work.

Throughout this and other books you will find that generic and specific names are always italicized, but names in the other categories are not. This is one of the rules of the Linnaean system. Another rule is that a specific name is never used without a generic name. For instance, we never say *familiaris* to designate the common dog. We say *Canis familiaris,* or write it *C. familiaris* after having introduced the generic name once. The generic name may, however, be used alone to designate the entire genus. Notice also that the generic name always begins with a capital letter, but the specific name starts with a small letter.

Eric Hosking from National Audubon Society

Alvin Staffan from National Audubon Society

Fig. 2.4 Top: Herring gull, *Larus argentatus.* Lower photograph, American Herring gull, *Larus argentatus smithsonianus,* is a subspecies of the common Herring gull. Notice that the subspecies is given an additional name. How would you define a subspecies?

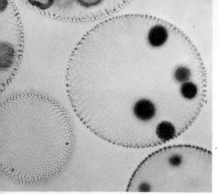

Ward's Natural Science Establishment, Inc.

Courtesy Car. Biol. Supply House

Fig. 2.5 Two common pond organisms, *Volvox* (top), and *Euglena*, which have characteristics of both plants and animals.

Fig. 2.6 Bushy stunt virus particles, photographed by means of an electron microscope, shown here magnified more than 50,000 times.

Photo courtesy Dr. R. C. Williams

A Difference Between Plants and Animals

If someone asked you to make a list of differences between plants and animals, what differences would you list? Write down three or four now. This may seem to be an easy and even useless task, since the common plants and animals are not difficult to place in their respective kingdoms. However, there are certain forms of plants and animals that are not so easily classified (for example the two organisms shown in Fig. 2.5), and the problem is not as simple as it might seem.

From an evolutionary standpoint, the first organisms were neither plants nor animals, at least if our assumptions about the origin of life are correct. Most biologists and biochemists are convinced that life began when certain complex molecules (such as nucleic acids) acquired the ability to duplicate themselves. In time, certain other molecules (such as protein) apparently became associated with them, and a given aggregate of molecules reproduced as a unit. Since they had the ability for **self-duplication,** these units can be said to exhibit life. The basic characteristic of life is that any living unit must be able to make more units like itself from chemical substances in its environment.

Some biologists believe that the first organisms resembled viruses. These extremely small units of matter are relatively simple compared with cells. A cell contains a great variety of chemical substances, whereas a virus particle consists only of a central core of nucleic acid (**deoxyribonucleic acid [DNA]** or, more rarely, a close chemical relative, **ribonucleic acid [RNA]**) surrounded by a coat of protein. We shall have much more to say about DNA in Chapter 3. Viruses (Fig. 2.6) do not carry on the complex chemical activities of cells, and they cannot even reproduce, unless they manage to get inside a cell. Whether they are living or nonliving depends on one's definition of "life." Their importance to our present discussion is that life probably had its beginnings from bundles of complex molecules with a structure similar to that of viruses.

Unhappily, the fossil record does not help us in our inquiry into the earliest organisms, simply because they could not be preserved intact. Present evidence indicates that the earliest organisms existed more than two billion years ago, and that it took them hundreds of millions of years to change into the complex forms of the first plants and animals. Apparently, some of the primitive forms never evolved a great deal further. It seems that they were so well adapted to changing environments that they have persisted to the present time. Since these organisms arose and apparently remained unchanged over the millions of

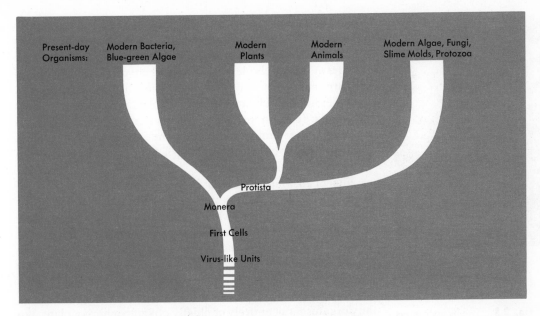

Present-day Organisms: Modern Bacteria, Blue-green Algae — Modern Plants — Modern Animals — Modern Algae, Fungi, Slime Molds, Protozoa

Protista

Monera

First Cells

Virus-like Units

Fig. 2.7 A schematic representation of one theory of how organisms evolved. This concept suggests that four kingdoms of modern organisms should be recognized.

years during which other organisms were evolving into new forms, it is these unchanging organisms that are so difficult to pigeonhole in what we call the "plant kingdom" or "animal kingdom."

In view of the existence of these organisms, some biologists recognize two kingdoms in addition to the plant and animal kingdoms, the **Monera** and the **Protista.** The kingdom Monera includes all organisms whose cells do not have definite or clearly formed central parts called the **nucleus** (plural **nuclei**). The two major groups of organisms so constructed are the **blue-green algae** and the **bacteria** (see Chapter 5). The kingdom Protista includes all one-celled animals (the **protozoa**), one-celled **fungi** and **algae** (other than blue-green algae), and a group of unusual organisms called **slime molds.** These groups are also described later. This classification of organisms is based on the possibility that evolution proceeded along the lines indicated in Fig. 2.7.

While this system of classification has a great deal of merit, and it does make us face up to the evolutionary problems of classification, we shall be content in this book to include all organisms in the traditional plant and animal kingdoms.

Setting this restriction for ourselves, how can we proceed with a list of differences between plants and animals? What about "mobility?" Can we say that animals move about, but plants

J. Carel

Fig. 2.8 Two insectivorous plants, sundew (above) and Venus fly trap (below). These autotropic plants are unusual because they "eat" insects.

Paul Popper Ltd.

do not? There are some animals (such as the sponges) that do not move about, and there are some plants (such as certain algae) that do; so mobility is not a valid difference. We might look for features at the cellular level that would help us. Most higher plant cells are enclosed by a rigid cell wall. The cells of most animals, on the other hand, are bounded by a soft membrane. However, there are so many exceptions that this distinction is no more valid than mobility. Most biologists feel that the nutritional habits of an organism come closest to making a valid distinction between plants and animals.

First of all, animals *eat;* that is, they take into their bodies foodstuffs that have to be digested before they can be used by the organism. Any organism which gains nutrition chiefly or entirely through eating is called a **phagotroph** (from the Greek words, *phagos,* "to eat," and *trophikos,* "nursing"). Let us turn the definition around and enlarge it slightly—any organism which is entirely or chiefly phagotrophic is an animal.

Obviously, according to this definition based on nutrition, any organism not entirely or chiefly phagotrophic is a plant. But this leaves us with two distinct modes of nutrition in the plant kingdom: 1. If a plant has **chlorophyll** (the green substance in plants), it can make its own food by using the energy of sunlight. By "food," we mean a potential energy-yielding material such as carbohydrate, fat, and protein. Such "independent" plants are called **autotrophs** (from the Greek words, *autos,* "self," and *trophikos*). 2. In contrast, plants that do not have chlorophyll must obtain their food from some outside source, as animals are obliged to do. However, unlike animals, such plants are incapable of eating as we defined the word. Instead, they must receive foodstuffs into their bodies molecule by molecule, that is, in solution. Such plants are called **heterotrophs** (from the Greek words, *hetero,* "other," and *trophikos*). Actually, there are some exceptions to these nutritional rules. For example, the plants shown in Fig. 2.8 are both autotrophic and phagotrophic. Nevertheless, a distinction is made based on nutritional habits of an organism. It does not solve all problems of distinguishing plants from animals, but it seems to work more consistently than any other single criterion.

Although this distinction based on nutritional habits of an organism does not solve all problems of distinguishing plants from animals, it seems to work more consistently than any other single criterion.

SUMMARY

Biologists classify organisms according to a hierarchy of categories that begins with the most general group (kingdom) and goes to the most specific group (species). This system has resulted largely from the work of Linnaeus, an 18th Century botanist.

More recently, the concept of evolution has stimulated taxonomists to strive toward natural systems of classification that rely on **genetic kinship**—that is, certain characteristics passed on from parent to offspring.

Some taxonomists recognize the kingdoms Monera and Protista, in addition to the plant and animal kingdoms. Under such a scheme, the Monera and the Protista are made to include those organisms having characteristics of both plants and animals.

However, most biologists distinguish plants from animals according to the organism's mode of nutrition. They are usually able to place any organism in either the plant or the animal kingdom on this basis.

FOR THOUGHT AND DISCUSSION

1 Distinguish between an *individual* and a *species*.

2 Write an improvement of this poor definition: a species is a group of similar organisms.

3 What is a "natural" system of classification as contrasted with an "artificial" one? Why is a truly natural system difficult to achieve?

4 A tiny organism named *Chrysamoeba* has chlorophyll and is thus autotrophic, but it also eats particles of food, and is thus phagotrophic. Would you consider it a plant or an animal? Does this indicate a need for recognizing more than two kingdoms? Incidentally, what taxonomic category does the name *Chrysamoeba* represent?

SELECTED READINGS

Simpson, G. G., and W. S. Beck. *Life: An Introduction to Biology* (2nd ed.). New York: Harcourt Brace and Company, 1965.

In this college textbook of general biology, taxonomy is placed in its proper relation to evolution.

Singer, C. *A History of Biology* (rev. ed.). New York: Henry Schuman, 1950.

An account is given of the historical development of the Linnaean system and of its modifications since the 18th century.

3 ADAPTATION: HOW ORGANISMS RESPOND TO THEIR ENVIRONMENT

Wisconsin Conservation Department; Madison, Wisconsin

Wisconsin Conservation Department; Madison, Wisconsin

Fig. 3.1 This bird, the ptarmigan, is pure white in winter and shows a pattern in summer. It lives in regions where snow covers the ground for much of the winter. How does this factor relate to its adaptation?

Each kind of plant and animal has a type of environment to which it is usually restricted (Fig. 3.1). Organisms are not scattered over the face of the earth in random fashion. There are good reasons why we do not find oak trees growing in the desert, or find polar bears roaming the wooded areas of North Carolina. All organisms are **adapted** to living in certain kinds of environments. Each plant and animal has structures related to its particular way of life, which is another way of saying that structure is a reflection of function.

Figure 3.2 shows a small desert animal, the kangaroo rat, which does not have to drink water at all. How it manages to survive under these conditions is a long story, but its body is structurally adapted to this kind of existence. From an evolutionary viewpoint, we do not say that the kangaroo rat has these structures *because* it lives in the desert; rather, we say, it is able to live in the desert because it has these structures. The same could be said for the structure-environment relationships of oak trees, polar bears, or any other organism.

In the preceding chapter, we considered some of the rules that biologists have established for dealing with the diversity which they find in nature. In contrasting artificial and natural systems of classification, we were concerned with how organisms differ from each other and in what ways they are similar. To put it another way, we were dealing with the "what" of nature. In this chapter let us consider the underlying causes of diversity, that is, the "how" of nature.

The Biological Meaning of Adaptation

Adaptation, in its simplest definition, is the ability of a species to survive in its particular environment. To say that organisms are adapted to their environment is to state the first axiom of ecology. If a species were *not* adapted to its environment, in order to survive it would have to move away or change. Otherwise it would become extinct.

Fossils, which are the remains or the evidences of dead organisms, show us that profound changes have occurred both in organisms and environments over many millions of years. Marine fossils found high in the Himalayas and other ranges show that before these mountains were thrust up they were once the floors of ancient seas. Fossils also tell us that a great number of plants and animals have become extinct over the millions of years during which there has been life on the Earth. Extinction seems to be the rule, not the exception. The number of living species in the animal kingdom is only one-tenth that of the fossil species. Time, then, plays an important part in adaptation. Equally important is the idea that adaptation is exhibited by species, not by individuals, for when we consider time, adaptation is more a process than a state of being. We sometimes say that an individual may "adapt" to different environments—for instance, if you move from the relatively cold climate of Montana to Florida—but this is not what the biologist means by adaptation. This is nothing more than adjustment through response to an environmental change.

Photograph courtesy: United States Department of the Interior, Fish and Wildlife Service

Fig. 3.2 A kangaroo rat shown in its native habitat. This animal is mentioned in the text because of its remarkable adaptation to desert life, but no explanation is given of those features which enable it to live without drinking water. What are these features?

Fig. 3.3 A group of prehistoric animals, including several dinosaurs, as they must have appeared some 175 million years ago. Why do you suppose these giant reptiles are no longer with us?

Peabody Museum of Natural History

Adaptation *as a process* means the ability of a group of organisms to develop, over a long period of time, certain structural and functional features which enable the group to survive and reproduce in a particular environment. The term adaptation implies change—some structural or functional feature of a group of organisms changes in such a way that it has adaptive value. Not only do we use the term *adaptation* to describe a process of change, but we frequently apply it to the result of that process. For example, the gills of fishes are an adaptation that enables these animals to receive oxygen from the water in which they live. The nectar produced by the flowers of many plants is an adaptation that ensures pollination by insects.

We say that organisms are adapted when they consistently produce enough offspring to ensure survival within their environment. If a type of organism cannot do this, as the dinosaurs (Fig. 3.3) could not, it becomes extinct. What chain of environmental events led to the extinction of dinosaurs is unknown. Yet we do know that these reptiles were successful for 100 million years.

The Origin of Adaptations: Evolution

It is one thing to observe diversity of structure and function among organisms, but it is quite another to explain it. Understanding the relationship between adaptation and environment is the problem. It is quite obvious that a fish could not live in water without gills or some equally efficient adaptation for taking oxygen from the water, and a desert plant could not survive in its environment unless it had water-conserving structures. If we say that fishes have gills *because* they live in water, or that cactus plants have fleshy, water-conserving stems *because* they live in the desert, this implies that the environment wields a modifying influence over organisms. Except in very special instances, this is not so. We must look elsewhere for answers to the question of origins of adaptation.

At least two centuries ago, naturalists began to be concerned with this problem. They began to wonder if the bewildering variety of plants and animals known to them had always existed. Had this great variety arisen full blown in nature? If not, where was the starting point? Most people who lived before the mid-1800's, including biologists, accepted a literal idea of special creation, and there they let the problem rest. But as biologists gathered more and more facts, their observations became increasingly more difficult to explain by the concept of special creation.

Among the most important new facts being brought to light

were those in the field of geology. In the early 1800's, the English geologist Charles Lyell published a paper that excited many biologists the world over. Lyell claimed that mountains, rivers, coasts, and all other land features are today changing and have always been in a constant state of change. As old mountains are worn away by erosion, new ones are thrust up out of the earth. Lyell cited evidence that such changes had been going on for thousands upon thousands of years. He was also able to show that the Earth was far older than was generally believed.

For some time geologists had had means of making reasonably accurate estimates of how long it took for certain rock and soil formations to occur. Fossil remains began to prove beyond doubt that organisms had lived on the Earth much earlier than the believers in special creation had thought. Furthermore, the fossil records revealed a wonderfully consistent trend—in general, the older the fossils, the simpler they tended to be in structure. The complex forms tended to be more recent in origin.

This discovery pointed to a process of gradual development of complexity. For example, when geologists examined the sides of a gorge, such as the Grand Canyon, they found fossils of complex plants and animals only near the top. As they examined fossils at greater depths in the gorge, the fossils were of simpler types. Proceeding toward the bottom, where the older rocks were, was like taking a reverse trip in structural complexity through the plant and animal kingdoms. See Fig. 3.4.

Before such discoveries had been made, a few biologists had conceived of a process of **evolution** to explain diversity. In essence, evolution means that nature is not static, but changing; it also means that organisms living today are the descendants of ancestors which were, at some stage of time, more simple in organization. One of the first biologists who advanced a theory of evolution was a Frenchman, Jean Baptiste Lamarck (1744–1829). In 1809, he published an account of his theory. In it, he said that evolution proceeds in relation to the use or lack of use of body parts. According to Lamarck, the continual use of a body limb, for example, strengthens and perhaps enlarges the limb, and this modification is passed on through inheritance to the next generation. Note the generations of rabbits in Fig. 3.5.

Lamarck's theory is known today as the theory of **inheritance of acquired characteristics,** and it is unacceptable to modern biologists. In fact, it never gained wide acceptance when Lamarck lived, partly because he presented his ideas at a time when very few other biologists were thinking about evolution. Furthermore, Lamarck could not support his theory by observa-

U. S. Geological Survey

Fig. 3.4 Grand Canyon, Arizona, showing fossil-bearing strata of rock. Formations such as this frequently show a continuous array of fossil organisms and their general tendency toward decreasing complexity as one proceeds from top to bottom.

1. At some point in the past, rabbits possessed rather short ears. Since their survival depended heavily upon their ability to hear an approaching predator, they stretched their ears continuously in order to hear with maximum efficiency.

2. The continual ear-stretching made an impression upon the reproductive cells, with the result that rabbits came gradually to have longer ears. These rabbits, in turn, stretched their ears, and passed the increase along to their offspring.

3. Eventually, a point was reached where ear length was sufficient to enable rabbits to survive without further stretching. At this point, ear length became stabilized.

Fig. 3.5 This is how Lamarck explained the evolution of ear length in rabbits. As you analyze the fundamentals of this explanation in the light of what you learn in this chapter, try to answer this question: Why is Lamarck's explanation not acceptable to modern biologists? Note the hypothetical steps listed above.

tion and experiment. It was, therefore, widely questioned. Although his explanation of evolution was inadequate, it did focus attention on the problem of explaining diversity in nature.

The year Lamarck published his theory a person was born who did more to popularize and clarify the concept of evolution than anyone who has lived since. He was Charles Robert Darwin (Fig. 3.6) of England (1809–82). In 1831, at age 22, Darwin set sail as ship's naturalist on H.M.S. *Beagle*. This five-year surveying voyage was to influence Darwin's thinking about evolution profoundly. It was during this time that he became aware of the exciting new discoveries being made in geology. This, in turn, influenced his thinking about the diversity and distribution of the plants and animals he observed during his voyage. He was especially impressed by what he saw on the Galapagos Islands (note Fig. 3.7) several hundred miles west of Ecuador in the Pacific Ocean. Here, as he traveled from one island to another, he noticed minute differences in related species of animals.

The finches (Fig. 3.8) fascinated him. He made a detailed study of the various finches, comparing and contrasting them. Generally, each island had its own finch species, slightly but definitely different from those of the other islands and the mainland of South America. How, Darwin wondered, did such diversity come about? The problem of the finches and other species of birds caused him to begin searching for an evolutionary explanation of diversity.

At the end of the voyage Darwin returned to England with a vast knowledge of plants and animals. As the writings of Lyell and other geologists had fascinated him, so did a book written by another English scholar. It was *An Essay On the Principle of Population,* by Thomas R. Malthus, an economist. Malthus said while human population increases geometrically, food supplies increase only arithmetically (Fig. 3.9). As a consequence, Malthus believed that there would always be a struggle for food, that in the world there would always be some people who would go hungry. Darwin was greatly influenced by this idea, and from it he formulated his theory of selection in nature.

Because he was careful and meticulous in his work, and because he was uncertain of the reception society would give to his ideas, Darwin spent more than 20 years developing his concept of evolution. It finally appeared in 1859 under the title *On The Origin of Species By Means of Natural Selection;* it was a book that eventually became established as one of the greatest influences of all time upon human thought.

Essentially, *The Origin of Species,* as the title is generally abbreviated today, set forth the idea that all present-day species of plants and animals came into being by a process of evolution. Darwin presented extensive evidence to show that evolution had occurred, and then advanced a theory explaining how it occurred. He called his theory **natural selection,** and he based it on four major points:

1. Variation exists within a species (have you ever noticed this in a litter of new-born puppies?).

Courtesy of The American Museum of Natural History

Fig. 3.6   Charles Darwin.

Fig. 3.7   A sketch of H.M.S. *Beagle,* on which Darwin served for five years as naturalist, and of the South American continent. Note the location of the Galapagos Islands, where Darwin made some of his most significant observations.

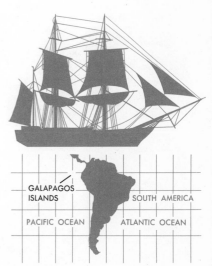

GALAPAGOS ISLANDS

SOUTH AMERICA

PACIFIC OCEAN

ATLANTIC OCEAN

Fig. 3.8 The several species of finches which occupy the Galapagos Islands. Each species is different in some discernible way, mostly in regard to beak shape. A close study of these differences set Darwin to thinking seriously about evolution as a likely explanation of diversity among species.

2. Overproduction of offspring is characteristic of organisms (a female *Ascaris,* a parasitic worm, is capable of producing as many as 200,000 eggs a day).

3. The less fit of the variants do not survive; nature "selects" the more fit, which reproduce (a strong puppy in a litter has a better chance of reaching maturity than a weak one).

4. Favorable survival traits (for example, general constitutional strength) are inherited by offspring from their parents.

Of these four points, the first two can be seen in nature, and Darwin provided many examples. The third and fourth points were logical conclusions based on his first and second points.

Every copy of Darwin's book was sold the day the book was published. Many scientists cheered Darwin's ideas and the publication of them, but there were some who condemned the book. Those who condemned it did so on the grounds that it attacked the widely-held belief that each species had originated in a series of creative acts on the part of a divine being. In contrast, evolution implied that life and its manifestations were subject to natural law. The argument was intensified, of course, by the realization that man, himself, had to be included in such a theory of evolution. Twelve years after his first book was published, Darwin published another one, *The Descent of Man,* which left no doubts about his thinking on man's place in nature.

Since Darwin's time, the concept of evolution in general, and his theory of natural selection in particular, have received a great deal of study. Virtually all present-day biologists accept the general principle of evolution, and there is no doubt that natural selection operates all around us in the plant and animal worlds alike. Nevertheless, it was not until more was known about genes and heredity that the basic causes of evolution came to be understood in detail.

A Bavarian monk, Gregor Mendel (1822–84), was the scientist whose experimental work led to an understanding of how certain traits are passed from parent to the offspring. It was not until 1900, after Mendel's death, that his work received wide recognition. Since then, it has become increasingly apparent that **genetics** (the study of how organisms inherit traits) holds the solution to the major problem of evolution that Darwin left unsolved. Darwin himself realized that his theory

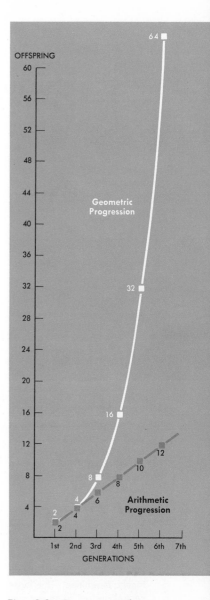

Fig. 3.9 By means of a simple graph, we can illustrate the difference in geometric and arithmetic progression. If Malthus's basic assumption is correct, it is not hard to see why life is a "struggle for existence." Darwin adapted this principle to natural selection.

The Granger Collection

Fig. 3.10 Gregor Mendel crossed different varieties of peas and discovered certain fundamental principles of heredity. Had Darwin known these principles, his theory of evolution would have been strengthened.

Fig. 3.11 Section of a cell, highly magnified. The large central portion is the nucleus; the dark patches are composed principally of DNA.

Courtesy Dr. G. Whaley

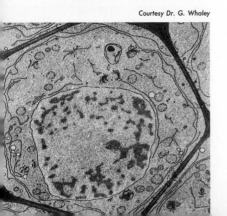

would have been stronger had he been able to explain the ultimate cause of variation and how traits are passed on from parent to offspring, but there was no help for it. We have no evidence that Darwin ever heard of Mendel, and both were dead before Mendelian genetics was known and understood.

The Biological Basis of Evolution

In recent years biologists have been able to explore on the cellular and molecular levels the means by which traits are passed on from parent to offspring.

Matter (whether living or not) is composed of extremely small particles called *atoms*. Most atoms do not exist singly within matter, but are joined to one another in the form of molecules. A **molecule,** therefore, is a group of atoms held together in certain ways. A substance such as common table sugar, for example, is composed of molecules, each of which is identical to every other molecule of the sugar.

Living systems, such as any complex plant or animal, are complex mixtures of thousands of different kinds of molecules. And on a higher level, the molecules are arranged in separate small units called **cells** (Fig. 3.11). Your body is made of several billions of these microscopic units. Typically, a cell contains a kind of governing body called the nucleus, which is suspended in the rest of the material that makes up the cell. When we study the cells of different organisms closely, we find a great many cellular and molecular similarities. This means that even the cells of oak trees and birds have *some* things in common. Most of their cells are similar in size; each cell has a nucleus, and each nucleus exercises the same kind of control over the rest of its cell. On the molecular level, many of the same chemical compounds found in the cells of birds are also present in the cells of oak trees. We can carry this thought even further and say that many of the same compounds are found in the cells of *all* living things.

Cells of all living things are similar to each other in one particularly important way. The nucleus of every cell of all organisms contains **deoxyribonucleic acid** (shown in Fig. 3.12) **(DNA).** All DNA molecules are large and complex compared with most other molecules. The reason DNA molecules are important to us in this book is that they are important parts of structures known as **chromosomes.** For many years, biologists have known that chromosomes are the carriers of hereditary determiners called **genes.** However, we have learned only within recent years that a gene is a certain portion of a DNA molecule.

Actually, no one has ever seen either a DNA molecule or a

gene clearly enough to tell much about their detailed structure. However, a great many indirect observations have enabled scientists to construct a model, or picture, of a gene and DNA. A DNA molecule seems to be a kind of double helix (spiral), with chains of atoms forming connections at regular intervals. Imagine a long ladder made entirely of flexible rubber and suppose that someone twisted the ladder until it looked like the structure shown in the DNA illustration. At the present time, this is our concept of the DNA molecule. It so happens that molecules of DNA are most unusual molecules. On occasion they can duplicate themselves precisely by building other DNA molecules from materials within the cell. Because they can do this, we find identical DNA molecules in both halves (daughter cells) of a dividing cell. The DNA molecule also seems to be "marked off" in different lengths, and each length is capable of "telling" the cell to make something. Each functional length of a DNA molecule is what we have been calling a *gene*. Particular genes you have inherited from your parents are responsible for your having blue eyes or brown eyes, black hair or blonde hair, and other features. (See Fig. 3.13)

Possibly you are wondering what all of this has to do with evolution, which we set out to discuss. Again, it is giving us a detailed answer to the problem Darwin was unable to solve. Genes affect their cells by giving them certain chemical messages. If a cell happens to be dividing and forming the embryo of a new organism, it is very important that certain chemicals form in the cell in certain ways. Otherwise, a developing human being, for example, might turn out to be a grasshopper, a cantaloupe, or a formless mass of cells. It takes thousands of chemical messages, each produced by the gene segments of a DNA molecule at just the right time in embryonic development, for an organism to be formed successfully. Organisms differ, therefore, to the extent that their DNA differs. For example, all human beings have very *similar* DNA; but except for identical twins, identical triplets, and so on, no two people have *identical* DNA in their cells. This is why so few human beings look exactly alike and why, in general, variation is possible within a species of plants or animals.

Biologists can now say with certainty that *external* variation, such as hair color, height, and so on is the result of *internal* variation dictated by DNA molecules. Variation, therefore, begins on the molecular level. Perhaps you are wondering if it is ever possible for a DNA molecule to make a "mistake" by producing a version of itself which is not an absolutely faithful copy. The answer is yes, and is perhaps the most exciting part of our discussion. When a DNA molecule makes a "mistake" in

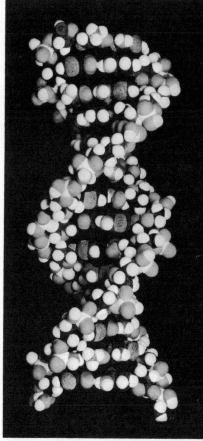

Abbott Laboratories

Fig. 3.12 A model showing the present concept of a DNA molecule (portion only). The fitted balls represent atoms. Note the double helix, as described in the text. DNA is the genetically active material of the cell.

Fig. 3.13 The common pigeon (middle figure) may give rise to variant forms. Darwin studied the artificial selection practiced by pigeon breeders of his day. Although genes and inheritance were not understood at that time, he arrived at an understanding of natural selection through his observations of pigeons and other domesticated animals.

duplicating a part of itself involving genes, we call the molecular change a **mutation.** But this seems to happen very seldom in DNA molecules—about once in 100,000 duplications for any given region, on the average.

Suppose there were a population of one species of animal in which every single member had ears six inches long. Suppose also that a mutation occurred in one of the animals and affected the gene governing ear length. Suppose further that the animal carrying the mutation produced offspring that had ears only one inch long. The offspring, in turn, would pass the "short-ear" gene on to certain of its offspring, and so on. Through mutation this population of animals would now have two varieties—one with long ears and one with short ears. What could happen to the short-ear variety through natural selection (perhaps you can guess) is extremely interesting, but this is getting ahead of our story.

As we said, once a mutation has occurred, the changed gene is transmitted as a portion of the genetic code from parent to offspring. Interestingly enough, most mutations do not benefit the organisms they affect; as a matter of fact, they frequently

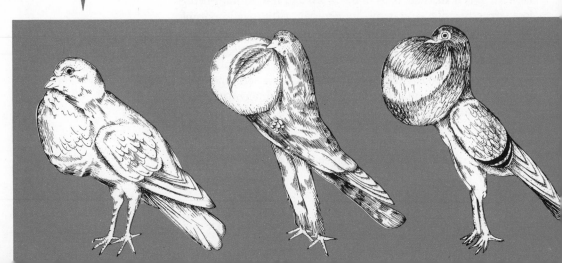

cause great disturbances in the well-balanced systems of DNA. Only rarely does a favorable mutation occur. But over the millions of years that this molecular trial-and-error process has been going on, along with great environmental changes, it has been sufficiently successful to give us the diversity we have on earth today.

It is time now for us to return to the role environment plays in evolution. One thing is certain—environment does not bring about evolutionary changes, at least not as Lamarck had thought. Numerous experiments have shown beyond doubt that the cells involved in reproduction are not influenced by other cells of the organism that may be changed by the environment. But perhaps you have read that x-rays and certain other kinds of radiation cause mutations by altering genes. This is certainly so, and if a group of organisms lived in a region constantly exposed to radiation sufficiently intense to bring about a large number of mutations, then the evolutionary future of the group would be affected. But on the earth, under normal conditions, this does not happen, so our statement that environment does not bring about evolutionary changes is generally true.

The environment is a *limiting* factor in evolution. It can prevent the success of certain genetic combinations while encouraging the success of others. And this brings us to the heart of natural selection. To illustrate, let us consider a particularly well-studied case of natural selection conducted over a period of years in England.

As long ago as 1850, insect collectors noticed that most moths found in nonindustrialized areas of England were light in color; fewer than one per cent were dark. Several decades later, after these same areas were industrialized, up to 90 per cent of the moths were dark (Fig. 3.14). Now, soot was deposited on virtually everything and killed almost all the lichens that commonly grow on tree trunks. The tree trunks themselves became covered with soot and turned darker in color.

Moths often rest on the trunks of trees when they are not in flight. As long as the tree trunks were light, and supported the growth of lichens (which themselves tend to be light in color), the lighter colored moths blended with their background and thus escaped detection by predatory birds. However, when one aspect of the environment changed (the color of the tree trunks), the lighter colored moths were no longer favored. Gradually, the dark form became predominant. It has been shown that only one or two genes control the production of dark pigmentation in moths, which simplifies our analysis of the problem.

To test this apparent case of natural selection, the English biologist H. B. D. Kettlewell conducted a series of studies on light and dark forms of the peppered moth, *Biston betularia.*

Courtesy of The American Museum of Natural History

Fig. 3.14 Dark and light forms of the peppered moth resting on a soot-covered tree trunk. Which of these moths has the better chance for survival in this environment? What does this tell us about the process of evolution?

Kettlewell released both light and dark moths in an industrialized area (Birmingham) and in a nonindustrialized area (Dorchetshire). He was able to show conclusively that far more light colored moths than dark ones are captured by birds on blackened tree trunks, while the reverse is true on tree trunks that are covered by lichens and are, therefore, lighter in color.

Because this is a particularly clear-cut case of natural selection, let us examine exactly what is involved. Since very few dark moths existed in the population before soot darkened the trees and other resting places of moths, the dark moths must have arisen as a result of random gene mutation. Had industrialization not taken place, the dark moths might have gone on maintaining the very small number in the particular species studied by Kettlewell, or they might have been eliminated entirely. However, as it turned out, a changed environment permitted an increasingly greater proportion of dark moths to survive, while it reduced the chances for success of the light forms. This is what is meant by natural selection. It does not produce or initiate genetic changes; this is the role of mutation. Natural selection merely tends to eliminate those individuals who are least fit, for whatever reason. The environment, then, is an important factor of natural selection in that it sets the standards for survival. (See rabbits in Fig. 3.15.)

Modern biology, with its emphasis on the cellular and molecular aspects of life, has done much to strengthen the principle that evolution is responsible for the great variety of organisms we see at the present time. Nature is not static, but ever-changing, and it is this change that we call evolution. Mutation and new gene combinations that come about through sexual reproduction allow varied DNA codes to express themselves in the make-up of an organism. The environment of that organism then plays an important role in determining whether it shall survive and reproduce, give rise to a superior and more successful race, or become extinct. Of this pattern, we are no longer in any doubt.

The differences that we see in organisms today are a reflection of some two billion years of change, both in the organisms themselves and in their environments. Whatever the origin of life may have been, it has expressed itself in the great diversity of our present world. All along the line, various groups of organisms proved successful for a time, and then disappeared. Extinction was the result whenever species were unable to live and reproduce successfully in their particular environments. So it has gone through the millions of years. Mutations arise constantly, new DNA combinations are brought into being through sexual reproduction, and organisms are continually

1. At some point in the past, ear length varied greatly among rabbits. Because rabbits are highly dependent upon hearing as a means of detecting the approach of a predator, those with short ears were at a distinct disadvantage.

2. In time, short-eared rabbits became fewer because more of them were caught and eaten. As a result, long-eared rabbits produced more and more of the offspring, passing the genes for ear length on to their progeny.

3. Since long ears constitute a successful adaptation in rabbits, those with short ears failed to survive the competition.

Fig. 3.15 This is how Darwin explained the evolution of ear length in rabbits. Compare this diagram with Fig. 3.5. Why is Darwin's explanation acceptable to modern biologists? (See steps listed above.)

put to the test of survival. Over time, natural selection determines the fate of individuals and species, and thus diversification continues. Some organisms and groups of organisms are relatively new on Earth. Others, such as the common cockroach, which lived at least 200 million years ago, have survived with very few changes.

This, then, is the biological explanation of diversity—on the molecular level of DNA, and on the broadest level of environment. Later, we shall have more to say about diversity and major pathways of evolution as they have occurred in time.

Courtesy of The American Museum of Natural History

Fig. 3.16 Mimicry in butterflies. The Monarch, shown at the top, is the model. The Viceroy is the mimic.

Some Special Examples of Adaptation

It is tempting to cite many examples of the curious or the unusual in nature, simply because truth is so often stranger than fiction. In this brief account, however, we must be content with a very few examples. Because of their significance in showing how adaptations arise in nature, let us now turn to three fascinating aspects of adaptation: **mimicry, camouflage,** and **convergence.**

A **mimic** is a person who imitates another person in dress, habits, mannerisms, and so on. In biology, mimicry means any close resemblance of the members of one species to another, especially when one species seems to derive some protection by appearing to be the other species. The species with some particular adaptation giving it special advantages is called the **model.** The species that derives an advantage by resembling the model is called the **mimic.**

A classic example of mimicry is found in the case of two butterflies, commonly called the Monarch and the Viceroy (Fig. 3.16). The Monarch seems to be distasteful to birds and other predators, who learn to avoid it in their search for food. The Viceroy lacks these distasteful qualities, but resembles the Monarch so closely that it is left alone by predators. The Monarch is thus the model, and the Viceroy is the mimic. Another example of mimicry is the striking resemblance of certain moths and flies, which do not sting, to wasps or bees. Mimicry is quite common among animals, and frequently the model may be a plant.

It is tempting to think that mimics deliberately copy the models in order to become better adapted to their environment. But this would be attributing to insects and other animals a degree of intelligence which they do not have, to say nothing of plants that demonstrate mimicry. We must search for the answer in some aspect of natural selection.

Mimicry seems to begin on the gene level through mutation, which is a matter of chance. Quite randomly, then, a gene mutation or a combination of mutations happens to give an individual, or a small part of a population, some resemblance to another species. Also quite by chance, in time, or immediately, that resemblance may provide protection or be of advantage in some other way to the mimics.

An advantage over other members of the population, however slight, will tip the balance within the population in favor of the mimics. Since the mimics become better adapted to their environment (which includes the model) than the less fortunate individuals who lack the protective mimicry, more mimics survive and reproduce. Eventually, unless something happens to stop the trend, only the mimics in the population will survive.

Actually, this is a simplified explanation; nevertheless, it makes the point that mimicry is one important means whereby some organisms adapt to their environment. Like all adaptive mechanisms, it is evolutionary in origin and serves as an excellent example of natural selection.

To most of us, camouflage is much more obvious in nature than mimicry is. All of us have experienced the difficulty of seeing certain animals against a background of plants to which they bear a striking resemblance, or known the difficulty of seeing a fish even in clear water. Figure 3.17 shows two examples of camouflage in nature. Obviously, animals which are difficult to see in their surroundings are protected from their enemies, and the adaptive value of camouflage is unquestioned.

From the standpoint of natural selection, camouflage is a form of mimicry, and is explained in the same way. The better an organism can remain hidden from its enemies or from those organisms upon which it preys, the more successful it will be in survival and reproduction. In the case of organisms which are not very well camouflaged, other adaptive mechanisms, such as speed or the production of offensive odors, compensate for this lack.

The third example of adaptive mechanisms is an evolutionary phenomenon called **convergence.** We can define it as the development of similarities between different species which occupy similar environments. It is most striking when it occurs between species not closely related.

The shark and the porpoise, for example, belong to animal groups that are only distantly related. Their evolutionary pathways separated millions of years ago. Most animals of the group to which the porpoise belongs, the mammals, are not aquatic. All the evidence indicates that the aquatic mammals (porpoises, whales, and so on) arose from land-dwelling ancestors. Sharks, in contrast, are members of a rather primitive group of fishes. In spite of such different origins, these two animals bear a very close resemblance to each other. (Fig. 3.18)

Since the porpoise and its relatives evolved more recently than the shark group, it is tempting to call this a case of mimicry. However, mimicry involves a striking similarity between two species only. The shark and porpoise are not unique in their features. All aquatic vertebrates resemble each other in form to a great extent, and we have chosen these two merely as examples of fundamentally different groups. The point is that the porpoise, like the shark, is streamlined. This "design" feature permits the animal to move swiftly through the water—

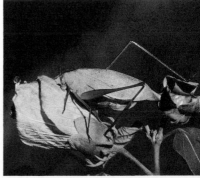

Courtesy of The American Museum of Natural History

Courtesy of The American Museum of Natural History

Fig. 3.17 Camouflage as illustrated by insects. The green color and shape of a katydid (top) make it almost indistinguishable from a leaf. The brown color and stick-like shape of the giant stick insect give it an appearance almost identical to that of brown twigs and branches.

Fig. 3.18 Convergence as it is illustrated by three distantly-related animals: a shark (top), an ichthyosaur (now extinct), and a porpoise. To what extent has environment played a role in the evolution of these three animals?

both as a means of escape from predators, and a means of catching other animals as a food source. In convergence, then, external resemblance in form between two or more different species is simply a reflection of environmental similarity, in this case, water. Perhaps our statements made earlier about environment and evolution are now clearer—a desert cactus does not have fleshy, water-conserving parts because it lives in the desert. It is able to survive in the desert because it has fleshy, water-conserving parts.

Convergence can be explained by natural selection just as mimicry can be explained by natural selection. Adaptation, no matter what form it takes, is a very complex aspect of evolution and many of the problems connected with it are not yet clearly understood. In some respects, we have not improved a great deal upon the insights of Darwin. One cannot read his *Origin of Species* without marveling at his powers of observation and his understanding of what he observed. However, by combining an ecological view with a genetical view—which Darwin was unable to do as well as we can today—biologists have come to understand the adaptation of plants and animals to an extent hardly possible only a few decades ago.

SUMMARY

Adaptation is the development of structural and functional features which occur in a sequence of organisms over a period of time, and which enable them to survive and reproduce within the limits of a particular environment. It is successful evolution.

In their adaptation, organisms have evolved a great variety of structural and functional characteristics. Many of these are developed in such a way as to be expressed in mimicry, camouflage, and convergence. Each of these phenomena can be explained by natural selection, but many aspects of adaptation are not yet clearly understood.

The diversity of living forms which we see on the Earth today is a result of some two billion years of evolution. This is a process whereby change occurs in the world of life, and as a result of this process, there appear new species which differ from their ancestral forms.

The initiating force of evolution is mutation, change that occurs at the molecular level in chromosomal DNA. Natural selection is the process whereby DNA "codes," or gene patterns, are proven successful. Diversity, as we see it reflected in the many kinds of plants and animals, is a result of diversity on the molecular level, since every organism undergoes development according to its particular DNA complement.

FOR THOUGHT AND DISCUSSION

1 It is possible to change the environment of paramecia, which are small water animals, by the gradual addition of salt to the water in which they live. After a time, they can live at salt concentrations which would kill other paramecia. In fact, they die if they are put back into the pond water. Is this adaptation? Explain.

2 Ask five individuals who have not taken a course in biology to define evolution. Write down their answers and compare them with the definition given in this chapter. Do these answers help explain why there is a great deal of misunderstanding about evolution?

3 One of the points made by Darwin in setting forth the principle of natural selection is that the fittest survive. Why would "fitness" have to be defined in relation to environment?

4 Define natural selection, basing your definition on the case of the light and dark moths described in this chapter.

5 What is DNA and why was it discussed in this chapter?

SELECTED READINGS

Dobzhansky, T. "The Genetic Basis of Evolution." *Scientific American,* Volume 182, January, 1950, page 32.

This article explains in some detail how mutation and the recombination of genes in sexual reproduction play an important role in evolution.

Odum, E. P. *Ecology.* New York: Holt, Rinehart, and Winston, Inc. 1963.

This small book, which is one of a series in general biology, sets forth the basic principles of ecology.

Simpson, G. G. *The Meaning of Evolution.* New Haven: Yale University Press, 1949.

This understandable book, written by one of the outstanding students of evolution in our time, will enlarge your grasp of the subject.

Singer, C. *A History of Biology* (see reference at the end of Chapter 2).

Those portions of this book that deal with evolution are appropriate to this chapter.

Wallace, B., and A. M. Srb. *Adaptation,* (2nd ed.). Englewood Cliffs, N.J.: Prentice-Hall, Inc., 1964.

This is a relatively brief discussion of adaptation and evolution.

4 THE ANIMAL KINGDOM

Most of us know much more about animals than we know about plants. Animals move about rather freely and, for other reasons, attract our attention and interest more readily than plants do. Furthermore, we are animals, so there is a natural temptation to compare ourselves in structure and function with other members of the animal kingdom. At some point or other, all of us have commented on similarities and differences between our own body and that of some other animal. In the pages that follow, we shall attempt to present the basic concepts of animal diversity. Armed with these concepts, you will then be able to pursue further studies on your own.

In Chapter 2, you learned that the earliest attempts at animal classification were made by Aristotle, and that he described only a few hundred species. You saw Linnaeus (Fig. 4.1) invent his system of binomial nomenclature and use it to describe certain similarities among organisms. In addition to the five taxonomic categories that Linnaeus used, "phylum" and "family" were added to accommodate the thousands of new species that were being described. In general, zoologists have had more success in drawing up a list of accepted animal phyla than have botanists for their plant phyla, or *divisions* as they are sometimes called in botany. Evolutionary relationships are somewhat clearer in the animal kingdom, and structural features are such that sharper distinctions can be made between animal groups than between plant groups. Nevertheless, zoologists disagree over the number of phyla that should be recognized, and no one listing is universally accepted. However, all the major schemes of animal classification are so nearly alike that the differences are minor ones.

Because it is representative, the system devised by Lord Rothschild is presented in Table 4-1. You can see that 22 phyla are listed, and that they include approximately 1,000,000 species. This is a conservative estimate; most zoologists place

Fig. 4.1 Carolus Linnaeus. (1707–78) Swedish founder of system of binomial nomenclature.

Courtesy of The American Museum of Natural History

TABLE 4-1. A Classification of the Animal Kingdom	
Phylum	*Approximate Number of Known Species*
Phylum 1. Protozoa	30,000
Phylum 2. Mesozoa	50
Phylum 3. Parazoa	4,200
Phylum 4. Cnidaria	9,600
Phylum 5. Ctenophora	80
Phylum 6. Platyhelminthes	15,000
Phylum 7. Nemertina	550
Phylum 8. Aschelminthes	12,000
Phylum 9. Acanthocephala	300
Phylum 10. Entoprocta	60
Phylum 11. Polyzoa	4,000
Phylum 12. Phoronida	15
Phylum 13. Brachiopoda	260
Phylum 14. Mollusca	100,000
Phylum 15. Sipunculoidea	275
Phylum 16. Echiuroidea	80
Phylum 17. Annelida	7,000
Phylum 18. Arthropoda	765,000
Phylum 19. Chaetognatha	50
Phylum 20. Pogonophora	43
Phylum 21. Echinodermata	5,700
Phylum 22. Chordata	45,000
	Approximate total: 1,000,000

Lord Rothschild, A Classification of Living Animals. New York: John Wiley and Sons, 1961.
Adapted by permission.

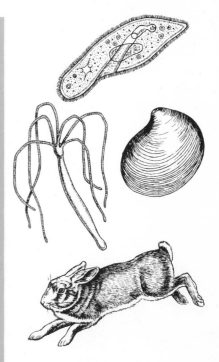

the figure closer to 1,250,000. Furthermore, on the average, some 10,000 new species of animals are described each year, which means that any estimate cannot be very accurate.

As indicated in Table 4-1, many phyla include a relatively small number of species. In fact, exactly one-half of those listed contain fewer than 1,000 species each. Three of them (phyla Mollusca, Arthropoda, and Chordata) account for nine-tenths of the entire animal kingdom! To look at the table still more closely, the phylum Arthropoda, which includes the insects, spiders, crabs, and various similar forms, is far larger than the other 21 phyla combined. As you will find in the next chapter, something similar occurs in the plant kingdom: The flowering plants (class Angiospermae) outnumber all other plants combined by about five to two (250,000 species out of a total of 350,000).

The scope of this book is such that we cannot discuss every phylum of animals. Some phyla include animals that most of us never see, and never shall see. Table 4-2 (see page 70) singles out groups that are important for our present purposes. These

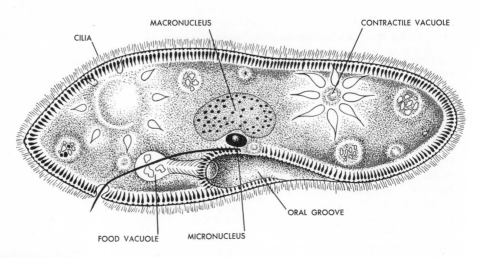

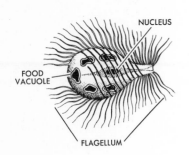

Fig. 4.2 Three representative protozoa: *Paramecium*, a ciliate (above), *Amoeba* (left), and a typical flagellate from the intestinal tract of a termite.

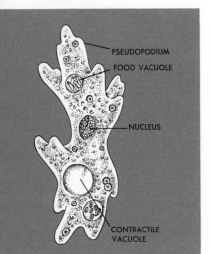

19 groups represent most of the known animal species, as you can see by the summary figure.

A SURVEY OF MAJOR ANIMAL TYPES

The Protozoans (Phylum PROTOZOA)

According to the **cell theory,** the fundamental unit of all living material is the cell. Most animals are composed of many cells and, therefore, are grouped in a subkingdom called the **metazoa.** Although some taxonomists recognize this group, the term is an informal one and is without taxonomic status. Metazoa simply distinguishes multicellular animals from those that are unicellular, or one-celled. This latter group has long been recognized as a single phylum, the Protozoa (Fig. 4.2).

Since the largest protozoans are barely visible to the unaided eye, we can learn little about them without a microscope. The entire group, consisting of more than 30,000 species, can be considered microscopic. As a matter of fact, most of them cannot be seen at all without the aid of a microscope, and some are so small that they are barely visible with the ordinary student microscope of 430 power. They are widespread in nature; both fresh and salt water abound with various species, and some forms live upon or within the soil. Still others are parasites of certain higher animals and are the cause of disease. For example, amoebic dysentery and malaria, both of which are widespread among humans, are caused by protozoa.

Order can be brought to the bewildering variety of protozoans by grouping the animals into classes according to their means of locomotion. Members of one class, which includes *Amoeba,* move whenever the cell contents flow in a given direction in response to a food source. An amoeba simply extends a "false foot," called a **pseudopodium,** and flows into it. Members of another class have many hair-like structures called **cilia** (singular, **cilium**) at the cell surface. Through the coordinated beating of their cilia, these animals can move rapidly through water. One of the most common ciliates, *Paramecium,* lives in most fresh-water ponds. A third class consists of protozoans that have one or more structures called **flagella** (singular, **flagellum**), which are much like cilia except that they are considerably longer.

Although many flagellates live in water, some of them live in the digestive tract of termites. These two species maintain an unusual relationship. Termites live on a diet of wood and are not able to digest cellulose, the tough cell wall material of most plants, but the protozoans can digest cellulose and do so within the intestinal tract of termites, thus benefiting the insect. Meanwhile the protozoans are provided with a suitable environment. Such a relationship is called **mutualism,** because it is a cooperative enterprise in which both species derive mutual benefit. A protozoan of the type described is shown in Fig. 4.2. In addition to the three classes of protozoans we have mentioned (*Amoeba* and its relatives, the ciliates, and the flagellates), there is a fourth class—*Sporozoa*—made up entirely of parasitic forms which do not have locomotor structures. *Plasmodium,* which causes malaria, is one such protozoan.

Although many protozoan species reproduce sexually, cell division is the usual method of reproduction. It has remained the chief reproductive method of protozoans throughout their millions of years of existence.

While protozoans are of little direct value to man, they play an extremely vital role in nature. Even though they represent a relatively small proportion of the animal kingdom in number of species, there are more *individual* protozoa than all other animals combined. In the water, they help to decompose organic matter by devouring bits of the remains of dead plants and animals. They also occupy an important place in nature's complex food web by serving as food for larger aquatic animals. Parasitic forms are of direct concern to man whenever they cause human diseases. The forms that produce disease in livestock, fish, or other animals in which man has a direct interest, are also important. Within the last few decades, protozoans

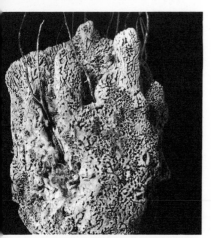

Courtesy of The American Museum of Natural History

Fig. 4.3 Some representative sponges. At first glance a sponge seems more like a plant than an animal. Why are sponges considered animals?

have been used widely in basic biological research. Since they are at once an individual cell and an organism, it is sometimes possible to discover in them fundamental principles that can be applied to higher organisms, including man.

The Sponges (Phylum PARAZOA)

If you could see sponges in their natural habitats, (Fig. 4.3) you might find it hard to believe that they are animals. Indeed, only a few decades ago they were considered plants because they did not move about. However, they have been included in the animal kingdom ever since biologists discovered that their cells are very similar to those of certain protozoa. Apparently, the various sponges evolved from protozoans—the cells of sponges being quite different, both in structure and in function, from any cells found in the plant kingdom. Actually, a given sponge is not so much an individual organism as a *colony* of organisms, that is, a group of protozoan-like cells living together in a common skeletal structure which they secrete.

Although a few species of fresh-water sponges are known, the vast majority live in the shallower waters of the ocean, especially in the warmer latitudes. A few are found in fairly deep ocean waters. Among sponges there is considerable variation in appearance and composition of the skeleton. In the skeleton of all forms are many rod-like structures composed largely of either calcium or silicon. In the group which is of commercial importance, a protein material called **spongin** makes up a large portion of the skeleton. Long after the cells of a spongin sponge have died, this material retains its texture, and allows for the absorption of water into the various canals that penetrate the skeleton.

Sponges reproduce both sexually and asexually. In organisms that reproduce sexually, there is a union of two cells (called **gametes**) resulting in a new single cell, the **zygote.** In sexual reproduction (Fig. 4.4) one sponge is able to produce both egg cells and sperm cells, but not at the same time. This assures cross-fertilization between two different individuals. Fertilization takes place inside the body of the sponge that produces the eggs, when the sperm from another sponge enter the canal system of the egg-producing sponge. The resulting zygotes swim out of the sponge and eventually attach to some object, or to the ocean floor, where they mature.

Asexually, some sponges produce buds, or little sponges, near their bases, and these eventually mature. However, they usually stay attached where they were formed. Large colonies of sponges may build up at a given point in this way. Sometimes, however, the mature buds may detach themselves and live independently. Figure 4.5 shows budding in sponges.

In other sponges, clusters of cells sometimes become separated from the parent sponge and are carried away by water currents. Eventually they attach themselves to some object on the ocean floor and grow to maturity. One particularly interesting thing about sponges—and about all metazoa to a certain extent— is their capacity for **regeneration.** This is the development of a new organism from a part of the body of the old organism, or it is the regrowth of a lost or injured part. A sponge may be cut into hundreds of small pieces, and if each piece is placed back in the water, it will grow into a complete sponge.

The Cnidarians (Phylum CNIDARIA)
also called (Phylum COELENTERATA)

The name of this animal group, which includes jellyfish, comes from the Greek word meaning "nettle." This is because all members have cells with small barbs, or stinging threads. Each barb, or thread, carries an irritating chemical which can be damaging to other animals. The larger jellyfish, some of which are six feet or more in diameter, can inflict painful and dangerous stings upon swimmers by releasing thousands of their barbs at one time. Even small jellyfish (a few inches in diameter) should be avoided. Figure 4.6 shows one type.

The cnidarians represent a very important advancement over the protozoans and sponges. For the first time we find the **tissue** level of organization, in which there is specialization of cells and cell groups.

Although fresh-water cnidarians are common, especially a small animal known as the **hydra** (Fig. 4.7), the most familiar

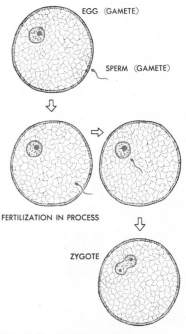

Fig. 4.4 Sexual reproduction of multicellular animals involves the union of male and female gametes to form a zygote.

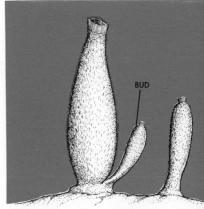

Fig. 4.5 Asexual reproduction in *Grantia*, a small sponge, by a process called budding. In most cases, the bud remains attached to the original sponge.

Fig. 4.6 A jellyfish, *Gonionemus*, with tentacles extended downward.

Courtesy Carolina Biological Supply House

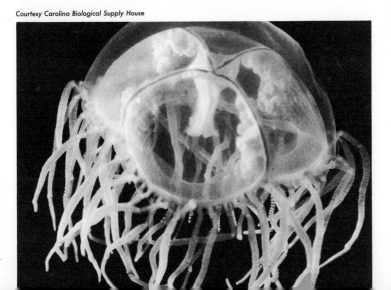

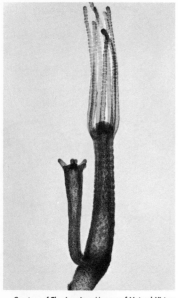

Courtesy of The American Museum of Natural History

Fig. 4.7 The hydra shown above has developed a bud which will break off and become independent. The diagram below shows a longitudinal section of a hydra.

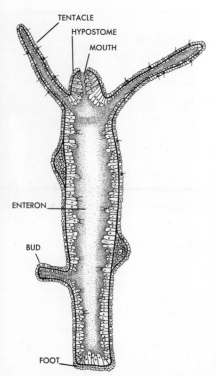

TENTACLE
HYPOSTOME
MOUTH
ENTERON
BUD
FOOT

form to us is the jellyfish. Another well-known cnidarian is **coral.** What we call "coral" is really the secretion of calcium compounds by a group of animals living in a colony. After the animals die, their colony of skeletons remains, and other coral animals may build upon them. In this way tremendous deposits form over a period of years.

The fresh-water hydras, which typify the cnidarians in structure and function, abound in fresh-water ponds. Barely visible to the naked eye, they live attached to the leaves and stems of water plants. Two layers of cells enclose a digestive cavity which has a single opening to the outside of the body. Some of the cells of the outer layer have the ability to contract. In this respect they resemble the highly specialized muscle cells of more advanced animals. By virtue of this contraction, the animal is able to change the shape of its body to capture food and to move about. The hydra has a network of specialized nerve cells that enable it to coordinate its movements and respond to stimuli.

Each individual can reproduce asexually or sexually. In asexual reproduction the animal produces buds, each of which eventually breaks off and becomes an independent animal. In sexual reproduction an individual usually functions as a male at one period and as a female at another. The single egg produced in an **ovary** (female sex organ) is fertilized by one of the several sperm that may swim to it after having been produced in a **testis** (male sex organ) of another hydra. The resulting zygote eventually develops into a hydra.

To biologists, cnidarians are important because they are the least complex animals which exhibit the specialization of cells into tissues, and because in general they have a high degree of regenerative power.

The Flatworms (Phylum PLATYHELMINTHES)

At one time in the history of zoology, nearly every invertebrate animal was called a "worm." Today, we generally restrict the term to those invertebrates whose bodies are elongated in the adult stage, and which move in such a way that the front, or **anterior,** end of the body leads the way, and the rear, or **posterior,** part follows along.

The flatworms are those worms whose bodies are much wider than they are thick. One class of the three generally recognized by zoologists is composed of free-living forms. A common example of this class (Fig. 4.8) is a group of worms known as **planarians,** which are easily collected from ponds and streams. The other two classes are parasitic, and are known as **flukes** and **tapeworms.** A tapeworm is shown in Fig. 4.9.

General Biological Supply House

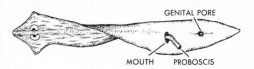

Fig. 4.8 Planarian worms. In the drawing (above) the worm is twisted to show upper and lower surfaces. Note the position of the mouth with the proboscis extended during feeding.

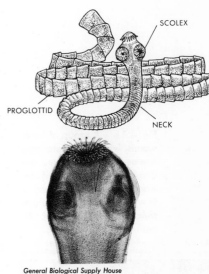

General Biological Supply House

Fig. 4.9 Diagram and photograph of a tapeworm, showing the "head" (scolex) and segments (proglottids).

In the free-living flatworms there are several well-developed body systems, including muscular and nervous systems. The digestive tract is essentially a sac with a single opening, although it is much more specialized and efficient than that of the hydra and other cnidarians. The most noticeable advance over the animals mentioned so far is the difference in over-all body plan. Flatworms, like most of the other animals we will consider, are **bilaterally symmetrical** (Fig. 4.10), as opposed to the **radial symmetry** of cnidarians and sponges. A radially symmetrical animal is built on a circular plan, somewhat like a wagon wheel. A bilaterally symmetrical animal is built on a longitudinal plan. Zoologists usually define a bilaterally symmetrical body as one that can be divided by one plane so that approximate mirror images are produced. Is the human body bilateral in its symmetry?

A few species of the free-living flatworms reproduce asexually by splitting longitudinally, but sexual reproduction is the general rule both in the free-living and in the parasitic forms. As a matter of fact, asexual reproduction is so rare in animals more complex than flatworms that we shall make no further

Fig. 4.10 A contrast in body plans. Many of the terms used to describe bilaterally symmetrical animals are meaningless when applied to radial symmetry.

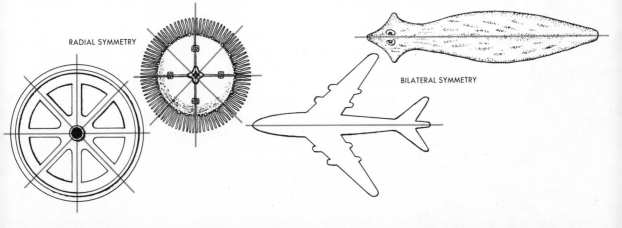

reference to it. Most flatworms have both ovaries and testes, that is, there are no separate male and female individuals among most flatworms. Planarian worms mate by exchanging sperm cells. After the eggs of each worm have been fertilized, they pass to the outside of the body. Each egg then develops into a small planarian which grows to maturity.

The flukes and tapeworms, all of which are **parasites,** are much more important to man than are the free-living flatworms. Several different species of flukes and tapeworms live within the bodies of domestic animals. They frequently do great damage, sometimes killing their hosts. Man can be a host to certain species of both forms. In certain areas of the world, especially where lax sanitation measures prevail, these two types of parasites are a major health problem.

The Nematodes (Phylum ASCHELMINTHES)

All the animals we shall discuss from now on have a digestive tract that begins with one opening (the **mouth**) and ends with another (the **anus**). Among the least complex of these animals are the Aschelminthes, a phylum containing a variety of forms. The most numerous of them are the nematodes, or roundworms (Fig. 4.11). Unlike the flatworms, nematodes have cylindrical bodies that are usually pointed at each end. Some are free-living and are found abundantly in fresh water and in soil. Others are parasites that use a variety of other animals, including man, as host.

Usually, a roundworm is either distinctly male or distinctly female. This is a new condition of sexuality in our survey of the animal kingdom. In each sex, the reproductive organs are in the cavity between the digestive tract and the outer body wall. During mating, sperm are transferred from the male to the female reproductive system, and eggs are fertilized inside the body of the female. Some female nematodes lay several thousands of eggs in one day. Under suitable conditions each egg develops into a small nematode worm which eventually grows to adult size.

Both plants and animals can be parasitized by nematodes. Many crop plants cannot be grown in some soils unless the nematodes are kept under control. Nematodes usually attack the roots, killing the plant or making it completely unproductive. Many roundworm parasites attack livestock animals and often produce fatal diseases. Quite a number also are known to infest the human body. How many of the following roundworms have you heard about: hookworms, trichina worms, the Guinea worm, and *Ascaris?*

Fig. 4.11 A group of hookworms, which are representative nematode parasites. See if you can find out why hookworm disease is not nearly as common in the United States today as it was a few decades ago.

Courtesy Carolina Biological Supply House

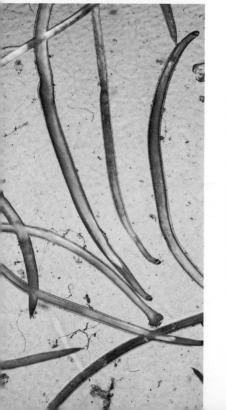

The Mollusks (Phylum MOLLUSCA)

As you saw in Tables 4-1 and 4-2, this is a very large group of animals. It includes a wide variety of forms, among them clams, oysters, snails, and octopuses (Fig. 4.12). Primarily, mollusks are marine animals, although there are many fresh-water and terrestrial snails, and there are fresh-water clams. A structure called the **mantle** is what sets mollusks apart from other animals. The mantle functions as a protective covering for soft and delicate tissues. In some mollusks—snails and clams, for example—the mantle secretes a hard, calcareous shell. If a mollusk has a single shell, like a conch or a snail, it is called a **univalve.** If it has a double shell, like oysters and clams, it is called a **bivalve.**

The various body systems of mollusks show a decided increase in complexity and organization over the animals we have already studied. The nervous and digestive systems, for instance, are more complex and efficient, and for the first time we find well organized circulatory and excretory systems. The octopuses and their close relatives, the squids, are particularly advanced.

Mollusks are essentially bilateral in their symmetry. The sexes are usually separate in a given species, although there are some exceptions. Most marine bivalves are males when they are very young, but they become females when they reach maturity. Sperm are usually released in the open water, and fertilization of eggs occurs within the female body whenever sperm happen to be taken into the body with a water current. In contrast, land forms must mate since there is no medium of water to carry the sperm from male to female.

The clam, which is representative of this phylum, has a number of specializations not present in the previous phyla we have reviewed. Much of the time, the clam is half or wholly buried in mud or sand. It moves by means of a muscular appendage called a **foot,** commonly miscalled the "neck." (In the more complex mollusks—the octopus and squid, for example—the foot has changed through evolution into a group of tentacles surrounding the head.) Two strong muscles attach the soft body to the valves, and by means of these muscles the clam is able to snap the valves closed as protection against its enemies. Two tubes, called **siphons,** extend to the edge of the valves. The clam draws water in through one of the siphons and expels it through the other. Food particles enter the animal this way, and waste material is expelled. Oxygen is also carried to the gills in the mantle chamber by the inflowing current of water. A good view of a clam is provided in Fig. 4.13.

Fig. 4.12 Representative mollusks: a common snail, an octopus, and a scallop.

R. H. Noailles

Douglas P. Wilson

National Park Service, Department of Interior

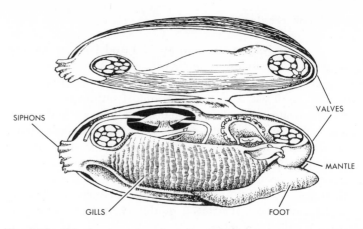

SIPHONS

VALVES

MANTLE

GILLS

FOOT

R. H. Noailles

Fig. 4.13 This drawing of a clam shows some of the complex internal anatomy typical of mollusks. The four circular structures shown at the ends of the two shell-halves are points where strong muscles attach.

Sperm entering the female clam on the inflowing current of water are carried to a special pouch in the gills. Here the eggs are fertilized and develop into **larvae** (worm-like forms) called **glochidia.** Eventually the glochidia leave the female on the outward flowing current and complete their life cycle.

Other specialized organs of the clam include a stomach and intestine, blood vessels, a heart, kidneys, a urinary bladder, and a nervous system. Mollusks, as represented by the clam, are strikingly complex animals compared with those of the phyla we have seen so far.

The Annelids, or Segmented Worms (Phylum ANNELIDA)

The bodies of annelids are divided into segments. This feature is so pronounced in them that it has become the chief means of distinguishing them from other groups of animals, even though certain other animals have segmented bodies—tapeworms, for example. There are several

Lynwood M. Chace

Fig. 4.14 Two common annelids. The earthworm (top) is shown at the surface of loose soil. The leech (bottom) is being eaten by a large diving beetle.

Fig. 4.15 This diagram shows part of the complex internal anatomy of an earthworm. Note especially the complexity of blood vessels.

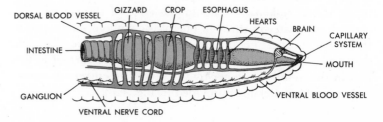

DORSAL BLOOD VESSEL   GIZZARD   CROP   ESOPHAGUS

HEARTS

BRAIN

CAPILLARY SYSTEM

INTESTINE

MOUTH

GANGLION

VENTRAL BLOOD VESSEL

VENTRAL NERVE CORD

thousand different types of annelids, including marine, fresh-water, terrestrial, and parasitic forms. The most familiar member of this group is the common earthworm. Another common annelid is the leech. Both of these are shown in Fig. 4.14.

The earthworm is fairly representative of this group. Externally, the segmented nature of the body is obvious, the segments often numbering well over a hundred. Internally, many of the organs and other structures of the body are repeated segment by segment, so that the animal is a series of fairly uniform "slices." In general, the body plan (Fig. 4.15) shows an advance in specialization and efficiency over the groups we have studied so far. The nervous, muscular, digestive, excretory, and circulatory systems are particularly advanced. The circulatory system, for example, consists of a series of closed tubes, or blood vessels. Blood is pumped through the vessel to other organs of the body by five pairs of **aortic arches,** or hearts. As in higher animals, food in diffusible form enters the blood through the walls of an intestine. Oxygen enters the bloodstream through the "skin," or **cuticle,** and is carried by the blood to other parts of the body. In a similar way, carbon dioxide is given off through the cuticle.

Many of the features of the earthworm are adaptations to its particular way of life and are not typical of all annelids. For example, marine annelids have eyes and other sense organs that earthworms do not have. Furthermore, earthworms do not have legs and certain other appendages that characterize marine annelids. Although the sexes are separate in marine annelids, this is not the case in earthworms. Every earthworm has both testes and ovaries. A pair of worms mate and exchange sperm. The sperm are then stored by each worm in a special receptacle for later use in fertilizing its eggs. The eggs are released from the body in groups and are deposited in the soil within cocoons. Each cocoon encloses several eggs. After a period of development, small worms emerge from these cocoons.

The annelids are not of great economic importance to man, with the exception of the earthworm. As it burrows through the soil, an earthworm forms canals through which air may pass. This permits chemical activities to occur in the ground at a much more rapid rate than would be possible otherwise. Furthermore, earthworms eat soil that is too hard to be pushed aside. As the soil passes through the worm's digestive system, a number of materials are digested or broken down into simpler forms. Through its several activities in the soil, the earthworm hastens the decomposition of dead and decaying matter, which increases soil fertility. The exact value per worm to the farmer would be difficult to calculate, but the presence of earthworms in the soil is highly beneficial.

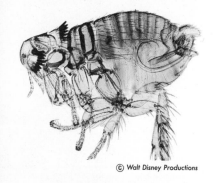

© Walt Disney Productions

P. A. Knipping

USDA

Fig. 4.16 Some representative insects. In general, insect species are rather easily distinguished because of their body structure. Top: rabbit flea. Middle: queen bee and her "court." Bottom: mayfly.

The Insects (Class INSECTA, Phylum ARTHROPODA)

The phylum Arthropoda (Fig. 4.16) is the largest in the animal kingdom. It is so large, in fact, that we will have to break it down into five smaller groups, or classes. All animals belonging to this phylum have jointed and paired appendages. They also have three jointed body segments called the **head, thorax,** and **abdomen,** although in some the head and thorax are fused. The internal organs of all arthropods (and most mollusks) are bathed in blood. This **open** circulatory system is quite different from the **closed** (blood vessel) circulatory system of the earthworm.

There are other important distinguishing features. A hard outside skeleton, called an **exoskeleton,** encloses the arthropod body. Sensory structures (particularly eyes) show a decided advance over the animals we have studied so far. In addition to other body systems being quite advanced, in all but a few arthropods the sexes are separate.

The insects, one class of this phylum, are by far the most numerous group among the Arthropoda, as shown in Table 4-2. The estimate of 700,000 known species is conservative; many zoologists use the round figure of one million. At any rate, there are more known species of insects than of all other animals combined. Insects exist in such variety that a general description of them is difficult, although certain features set them apart from other members of their phylum. They are distinguished from other arthropods by having three pairs of walking appendages in the adult stage. Most of them also have wings in the adult stage (usually two pairs). This is not true of any other invertebrate animals. The ability of insects to fly helps explain their success as an animal group. Although most insects are found in terrestrial-aerial habitats, a great many species live in water (the immature stages of many land-dwellers are also aquatic), in the soil, and as parasites. Virtually none are marine.

Some insects, such as the grasshopper and its near relatives, develop from eggs and pass only through a **nymph** stage before becoming adults. In the nymph stage they are near carbon copies of an adult, except that the nymphs are smaller. Most other species of insects go through a more complicated life cycle. Since butterflies are typical of this latter group, we shall describe their life cycle (shown in Fig. 4.17) briefly.

After the female butterfly mates with a male, she lays fertilized eggs on leaves or other vegetation. The eggs hatch into caterpillars (the larval stage), which bear no resemblance to the adult butterfly. In moths and butterflies, the larva is called a **caterpillar.** After a period of intense feeding and rapid growth, the larva spins a cocoon around itself and becomes

dormant for several days, weeks, or months, depending on the species. At this stage, it is called a **pupa.** Although a pupa looks inactive, many internal changes are taking place. Finally, a fully mature butterfly emerges from the cocoon, dries its wings, and mates, thus starting the cycle anew.

The economic importance of insects ranks exceedingly high. The honey bee and the silkworm moth are probably the most beneficial of all insects, at least in a direct sense. Indirectly, many insects serve to pollinate various flowers, including those of some crop plants. Their value in this role is inestimable.

Several insects are valuable to man because they prey upon other insects. From the standpoint of damage, a great number of different forms prey upon crop plants. A swarm of locusts can completely destroy a farmer's crop in a matter of minutes. Almost every species of plant has insect enemies. It is a rare orchard or farm crop that does not have to be sprayed in order to produce a respectable yield. Various flies and lice inflict great damage on livestock animals and frequently transmit infectious diseases. Insects also are responsible for carrying many diseases to man. For example, the protozoa which cause malaria are transmitted to man by certain mosquitoes.

From an ecological viewpoint, insects are the dominant animals on Earth today. They are the "dinosaurs" of the 20th century. Among all organisms, they are probably the only group that poses a threat to man's continued existence as a species, and we can do amazingly little to reduce the threat.

The Crustaceans (Class CRUSTACEA, Phylum ARTHROPODA)

Unlike the insects, crustaceans (Fig. 4.18) have five or more pairs of walking appendages, and two pairs of sensory appendages. The large pair are called **antennae,** and the small pair, **antennules.** Insects, you will recall, have only a single pair. The exoskeleton of crustaceans is generally heavier than that of insects. Most species are marine, although several inhabit fresh water or land. Typical marine forms are the lobsters, shrimp, and crabs. The crayfish (Fig. 4.19) is perhaps the best-known fresh-water type, and the bluish-gray sowbug (Fig. 4.18C) is a common terrestrial form.

Lynwood M. Chace

Fig. 4.17 Three stages in the metamorphosis of a butterfly. Top: larvae, or "caterpillars." Middle: pupa. Bottom: adult emerging from pupa case.

As we have done with the other classes of this phylum, let us select one typical animal and take a detailed look at one aspect of it in order to see still another way in which this phylum exhibits complexities over the simpler animals of earlier phyla. The digestive system of the crayfish, which is a common laboratory animal, will serve as an example. Crayfish eat animals and plants, and are, therefore, said to be **omnivorous.** Several specialized appendages associated with the mouth are

R. H. Noailles

U.S. Fish and Wildlife Service—Rex Gary Schmidt

Courtesy of The American Museum of Natural History

Fig. 4.18 Some representative crustaceans. Left: a shrimp in natural pose. Above: a land crab walking on sand. Right: a sowbug, or "roly-poly."

used to manipulate, tear, and chew bits of food. From the mouth the food is forced into the first part of a double stomach. Teeth lining this part of the stomach, called the **gastric mill,** grind the food into smaller pieces. Stiff hairs in the second part of the stomach strain out bits of food that are too large to pass. The finely divided pieces are permitted to enter the intestine where they are broken down to a diffusible form by strong digestive juices supplied by the liver. The food, now digested, passes through the intestinal walls into the blood surrounding the intestine.

Fig. 4.19 Internal anatomy of a crayfish. Note the ventral position of the nerve cord, which is typical of invertebrate animals.

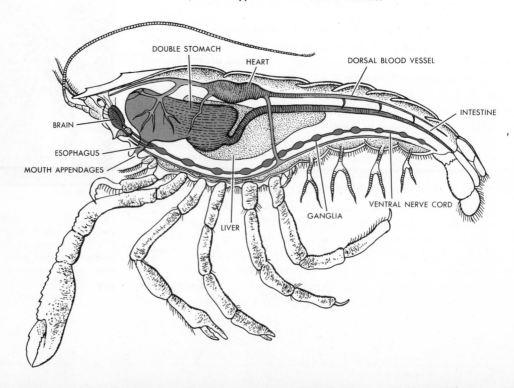

In nature, crustaceans are important in the over-all food web. Many small forms of both fresh and salt water crustaceans consume tiny plant organisms called **algae.** In turn, the crustaceans are themselves eaten by larger animals. The sole food of the blue whale, the largest living animal, is a small shrimp-like crustacean. It has been estimated that in its lifetime one blue whale eats 10,000 tons of these small animals. Other whales, other marine animals, and men also use crustaceans as a food source. In this way, crustaceans serve as an important link in the general food web of nature.

USDA Photo

The Arachnids (Class ARACHNIDA, Phylum ARTHROPODA)

Spiders and the other members of this group are distinguished from other arthropods by their four pairs of walking legs and absence of antennae. In addition, a pair of appendages just in front of the legs serve as poison claws in most arachnids. The mouth parts are not adapted for biting; hence, the bite of a spider is really a pinch of the poison claws. Other familiar forms include scorpions, harvestmen ("daddy longlegs"), ticks and mites, and the king, or horseshoe, crab. See Fig. 4.20.

The spiders are the most numerous of the arachnids. Many people fear spiders, but most spiders are entirely harmless. There are only two dangerous species in the United States. One is the black widow, whose bite is occasionally fatal, especially to small children. The other is the brown recluse, whose bite is not fatal, but which causes the flesh in the bite area to decay. The large tarantula of the southern United States is greatly feared, but its bite usually causes little more damage than pain. Although all spiders are equipped with poison claws, the amount of poison injected is usually so small and of such low toxicity to humans that it causes no more than a small amount of pain and redness.

Scorpions (Fig. 4.21) are another matter. Outwardly they resemble crayfish. They are unusual in having a sting at the end of the abdomen. Although most of the 40 or so species found in the United States can deliver a painful sting to man, only two are dangerous. All of them are capable of killing animals much larger than themselves. Most scorpions of the United States are restricted to the warmer areas of the country, particularly to the Southwest.

Ticks and their close relatives, the mites, are very numerous and widespread (Fig. 4.22). All are parasites on bodies of higher animals, with the exception of a few free-living mites. It is a rare bird or mammal, that is not afflicted at one time or another with some species of tick or mite.

Mites in tremendous numbers may infest a chicken. They

© Walt Disney Productions

Fig. 4.20 Black widow spider, showing relative size of male (smaller) and female (larger). Below: a diving water spider beginning to submerge.

Fig. 4.21 Scorpion with abdomen poised in the sting position.

© Walt Disney Productions

Courtesy Carolina Biological Supply House

Fig. 4.22 A representative tick. Why are ticks considered more closely related to spiders than to insects?

Courtesy of The American Museum of Natural History

Fig. 4.23 Centipedes. How many legs do the "hundred-leggers" shown here have?

Fig. 4.24 A millipede. Can you figure out the sequence of leg motion which this animal employs as it moves along?

Courtesy of The American Museum of Natural History

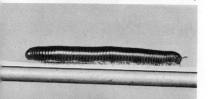

live by sucking blood out of the fowl, which lowers egg production drastically and may eventually cause the chicken's death. Ticks and mites also carry microorganisms that are responsible for diseases in man, in domestic animals, and in plants. Among the more important of these diseases are Rocky Mountain spotted fever and tularemia, both of which are contracted by man and a variety of animals, and Texas fever, which is a disease of cattle. Most people have experienced an attack of chiggers, or "red-bugs," which are also a form of mite. They are extremely small, and their bite produces a red, itching welt on the skin.

The Centipedes (Class CHILOPODA, Phylum ARTHROPODA)

If the centipedes and their close relatives, the millipedes, were not clearly arthropods, we would be tempted to call them annelid worms. The centipede's elongated body has many segments, each one of which (except the first and last) has a single pair of legs. So many walking appendages has given rise to the common name "hundred-legger." The exact number of legs depends, of course, on the number of segments. On the first segment behind the head is a pair of poison claws which resemble those of spiders. A single pair of antennae projects forward from the head. See Fig. 4.23.

Centipedes invade nearly any dark place. Small forms are often seen under logs, piles of straw, or old boards. Many species invade houses. In the tropics, it is not unusual to find centipedes a foot long. These larger forms can give a painful bite. In fact, it is wise to avoid even small centipedes. One of the first things campers in the tropics learn is not to walk barefoot around temporary quarters and not to put on shoes in the morning without first making sure that a centipede has not crept in during the night. Except for being a minor menace, centipedes are of little importance to man. They do, however, eat certain harmful insects, which makes "hundred-leggers" of some value.

The Millipedes (Class DIPLOPODA, Phylum ARTHROPODA)

Millipedes are very much like centipedes in appearance and structure. Their internal anatomy is strikingly similar. However, there are enough differences to make most zoologists prefer to place the two in separate classes. One of the most obvious differences is that millipedes have *two* pairs of legs on each segment, whereas centipedes have only one pair. Furthermore, millipede legs are much shorter than those of centipedes. This seems to account for the relative slowness of movement of millipedes, while centipedes, in contrast, move rapidly. Although millipedes are sometimes called "thousand-leggers," they seldom have more than 100 segments, not all of which have appendages; see Fig. 4.24 for example.

In contrast to the centipedes, which are **carnivorous** (that is, they eat other animals), millipedes are **herbivorous** (plant eaters). The difference in rate of travel between the two types of animals is a reflection of their different feeding habits. From an evolutionary standpoint, herbivorous animals are not under pressure to move about fast—at least not in their search for food. Natural selection, then, would not weed them out for their slowness. Some slow moving animals, however, may be under pressures to escape from faster moving enemies that would eat them, but the millipede has "solved" this problem in another way. When it is disturbed, it curls up and plays dead. Furthermore, most species of millipedes have glands that produce offensive fluids, so there are few animals that care to eat them.

Millipedes are of no particular importance to man since they feed upon dead vegetation. In this respect, of course, they help to decompose plant materials in nature. Unlike the centipedes, they have no poison claws, and they are entirely harmless.

The Echinoderms (Phylum ECHINODERMATA)

You will recall that the sponges and cnidarians, which are relatively simple animals, are radially symmetrical in their body structure. You also found that later groups, relatively more complex, are bilaterally symmetrical. For years, biologists believed that radial symmetry was a reliable indicator of relative simplicity. For this reason, echinoderms were once placed far down in the scale of animal complexity. However, when embryology and biochemistry came into their own, biologists learned that: 1. echinoderms are very similar to chordates (the highest phylum consisting of the most complex animals) in the way they develop, and 2. their body fluids bear a closer chemical resemblance to those of chordates than do the body fluids of any other invertebrates.

To look again at the matter of symmetry, the larvae of echinoderms *are* bilaterally symmetrical, but on their way to becoming adults they switch over to a radial plan. Even so, modern zoologists are convinced that echinoderms are more closely related to the chordates than to the less complex invertebrates. This is another way of saying that their evolution is more closely linked to the highest animal phylum than to lower ones.

Fig. 4.25 Representative echinoderms. Top: sea urchin. Middle: starfish. Bottom: sea cucumber. Note the rough exterior surfaces and the radial symmetry.

P. A. Knipping

United States Department of the Interior, Fish and Wildlife Service

Courtesy Carolina Biological Supply House

Exactly what are echinoderms? The name itself means "spiny skin," and this is a fairly good description of one obvious characteristic of the group. They are very rough to the touch, because their outer body wall is thoroughly covered with small, calcareous spines. Body systems of echinoderms are not as well developed as those of mollusks, annelids, and arthropods, and sense organs in particular are poorly advanced. All forms of echinoderms are marine, and they are found both in shallow and in fairly deep waters of the ocean. Some common echinoderms, sea cucumbers, sea urchins, and starfish are shown in Fig. 4.25.

In their reproduction, the sexes are separate in all but a few species. However, no mating process occurs between male and female individuals. Eggs and sperm are released into the water and fertilization takes place somewhat by chance outside the body. A zygote develops into a larva which is bilaterally symmetrical. By a very complex process of growth, the larva develops into a radially symmetrical adult.

Echinoderms are of almost no positive economic importance, although sea cucumbers are eaten in some parts of the world. Any oyster fisherman can tell you about the negative economic importance of starfish. These echinoderms prey upon mollusks to such an extent that oyster fishermen are obliged to wage war upon them to prevent the complete destruction of their oyster beds. A large starfish can easily consume five good-sized oysters in a day. It eats an oyster by folding itself around both sides of the shell, to which it attaches by its hundreds of little hydraulic suction cups called **tube feet.** Eventually, through fatigue, the oyster relaxes its muscles. Its shell is then easily opened (Fig. 4.26). The adaptable starfish then everts its own stomach and pushes it between the two halves of the shell, and proceeds to digest the fleshy body of the oyster.

When oyster fishermen first became aware that they were competing with starfish, the fishermen tried to deal with the problem by catching large numbers of starfish, cutting them up, and throwing the pieces back into the water. What they did not realize is that starfish and other echinoderms have great powers of regeneration. A starfish hacked into three pieces in the right way grows into three new starfish! The hapless fishermen were simply aiding the enemy. At the present time, chemical methods are used to protect oyster beds from starfish. When fishermen catch starfish now, they either throw the animals on the beach to die in the sun, or sell them to laboratories.

Even though echinoderms are of little commercial value, and are a downright menace to the oyster industry, there is one bright spot in their existence. Since the eggs of echinoderms

Fig. 4.26 A starfish attacking an oyster. The starfish continues to pull the valves apart until the oyster's muscles relax with fatigue.

Department of the Interior, Fish and Wildlife Service

develop in open water, where they can be observed, they are important to embryologists. This is especially true since echinoderm development parallels so closely that of the chordates, including (to a certain extent) man himself. Some of the basic principles of embryology were discovered many years ago through study of starfish and sea urchin eggs. Furthermore, any animal that is capable of a high degree of regeneration is useful to biologists. There is still much for us to learn about the regeneration of tissues and the healing of wounds.

The Protochordates
(Classes UROCHORDATA, CEPHALOCHORDATA; Phylum CHORDATA)

At some point in evolutionary history, we are not sure where or when, a small group of animals began to undergo drastic changes. Eventually the changes gave rise to a new group of animals, the chordates, (Fig. 4.27) that were unlike anything else in the animal kingdom. There is no way of knowing with certainty what kinds of animals gave rise to the chordates. They may have been annelid-like, as some zoologists think. It seems evident that both chordates and echinoderms evolved from a common worm-like ancestor of some sort. According to fossil evidence, the change took place about 500 million years ago. Since that time chordates have gradually become the numerous and highly diversified group of animals, including man, that we know today.

The chordates kept some of the more successful features that we see in some of the other phyla—for example, bilateral symmetry, and some degree of segmentation. But there are three major structural features that chordates do not share with any other phylum of animals.

1. A structure called a **notochord** appears in the embryonic stage as a stiff rod of cells (Fig. 4.28) just beneath the dorsal surface and running parallel to the long axis of the body. In the simplest chordates the notochord remains throughout their lives. In the higher chordates the notochord disappears and is replaced in the adult stage by a series of vertebrae. It is for this structure that the phylum is named.

2. **Gill clefts** form near the anterior end of the animal during its early stages (Fig. 4.29). These clefts become slits in those chordates, such as fishes, that breathe by means of gills. In higher chordates, such as man, the gill clefts are modified into other structures.

3. All chordates have a dorsal tubular nervous system that remains with them throughout their lives.

In those animals we have studied so far, in which the

Fig. 4.27 Two common forms of protochordates, each representative of a different class. Below: a large group of sea squirts, shown somewhat smaller than natural size. Bottom: amphioxus, about natural size.

R. H. Noailles

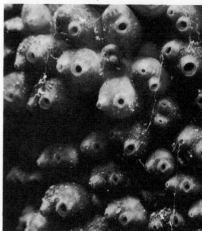

Lamort Geological Observatory

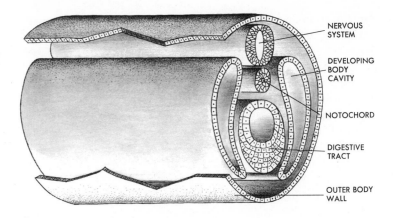

NERVOUS
SYSTEM

DEVELOPING
BODY
CAVITY

NOTOCHORD

DIGESTIVE
TRACT

OUTER BODY
WALL

Fig. 4.28   A diagrammatic representation of development in a chordate showing relative positions of the notochord and nervous system to other structures.

Fig. 4.29   The gaseous exchange system in fishes. The gill filaments expose a large area of blood to the water.

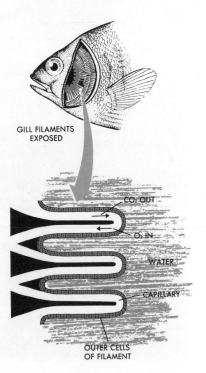

GILL FILAMENTS
EXPOSED

CO₂ OUT

O₂ IN

WATER

CAPILLARY

OUTER CELLS
OF FILAMENT

nervous system is at all advanced, the nerve cord lies near the ventral body wall, and is a solid mass of tissue. Thus, we find two features (notochord and gill clefts) that may or may not persist into adult stages of chordates, and one (the dorsal, tubular nervous system) that is present throughout life in all forms.

In addition to these three characteristics that set chordates apart from all other phyla of animals, there are certain others. Muscular, nervous, circulatory, excretory, and digestive systems reach a high point of specialization in the chordates. In most cases, there is a beautiful sequence of increasingly complex structures as one proceeds from the oldest to the most recent chordate animals. Sexes are almost always separate. In aquatic forms, egg fertilization usually (but not always) takes place in the open water, whereas a mating process is necessary in land-dwellers in order that sperm may be introduced into the female body by the male.

Many zoologists recognize two subphyla within the phylum Chordata: Protochordata and Vertebrata. Protochordates are those animals whose notochords persist throughout life and are never replaced by a vertebral column. The notochord serves as a sort of internal skeleton in these animals. In the vertebrates, a more efficient **endoskeleton,** composed of bone, cartilage, or a combination of the two, succeeds the embryonic notochord.

The protochordates are not very numerous, and most people never see them at all. The most common forms are the sea squirts, and a small marine animal known as amphioxus. Sea squirts (tunicates) are non-motile, jelly-like forms that grow in masses on pier supports or on the bottoms of ships. Many of them resemble boiled onions in appearance. Amphioxus is a small lance-shaped animal about an inch or more long that spends most of its life with its anterior end protruding from the floor of the ocean. It is usually found in shallow areas.

None of the protochordates are very important to man, although amphioxus is eaten by people who live along the coast of China. To biologists, however, the protochordates are a very important group. They are an important link between the invertebrate phyla that we have studied and the vertebrate members of the phylum Chordata.

Courtesy: Carolina Biol. Supply House

Fig. 4.30 Lamprey attached to a solid surface by its suctorial mouth.

The Fishes (Classes AGNATHA, CHONDRICHTHYES, OSTEICHTHYES; Phylum CHORDATA)

All aquatic vertebrates that breathe by means of gills only are called fishes. There are more species of fishes than of all other vertebrates combined (Table 4-2). The fishes are very old. For well over 400 million years they have been a successful group of animals. Their oxygen needs are met by removing oxygen directly from the water around them by the use of gills. Their body systems reflect the aquatic mode of life and a great many unusual adaptations to existence in water are seen in various forms. For taxonomic purposes, three classes are generally recognized.

The class Agnatha includes those fishes whose mouths are **suctorial** and lack jaws. The most common agnathan is the lamprey, misnamed the lamprey "eel." (This is a misnomer because eels are bony fishes.) The lamprey, like all agnathans, does not have scales. Although lampreys are sometimes used for food, commercial fishermen regard them as a menace because they attack and kill more edible fishes. See Fig. 4.30.

The class Chondrichthyes is made up of fishes which have jaws and scales, and whose skeletons are composed entirely of cartilage. Although agnathans also have cartilaginous skeletons, they do not have jaws and scales. Skates, rays, and sharks are typical of this class (Figs. 4.31 and 4.32)—entirely marine and widespread in the ocean. Sharks tend to be vicious animals. At many beaches they are a threat to human life, especially if a swimmer is losing blood. Some rays have a poisonous barb on their tail. With it they can deliver a painful and dangerous sting to their victims, including humans. Other rays can deliver strong electric shocks. The meat of certain sharks and rays is edible, and shark liver is processed for its oil. In general, the cartilaginous fishes are more harmful than valuable, so far as man is concerned, chiefly because they destroy large numbers

R. H. Noailles

Fig. 4.31 A typical ray. Note that its body is flattened dorso-ventrally.

Fig. 4.32 An adult sand tiger shark in characteristic swimming pose.

New York Zoological Society Photo

E. P. Haddon, U.S. Fish and Wildlife Service

Fig. 4.34 This bony fish, the largemouth black bass, is a favorite with sportsmen in a large part of the United States.

U.S. Fish and Wildlife Service

Fig. 4.33 A representative bony fish, the carp. Note mouth, adapted to bottom feeding.

Fig. 4.35 Modern lung fishes can obtain oxygen directly from the air (or from water). They employ this ability to survive out of water when the tropical streams and lakes in which they live temporarily dry up.

Courtesy of The American Museum of Natural History

of valuable food fishes, crabs, and lobsters.

The class Osteichthyes (Figs. 4.33 and 4.34) includes those fishes whose skeletons are composed largely of bone, which is a characteristic of the remaining vertebrates. Members of this class usually have scales, but of a type different from those of the cartilaginous fishes. There are also other important differences.

At least 20,000 species of the 23,000 listed for all fishes (see Table 4-2) belong to the Osteichthyes. Few groups of animals show a greater variety of size, shape, color, and unusual adaptive mechanisms than do the bony fishes. In size they range from certain tropical fishes a fraction of an inch long to the Russian sturgeon which may be 20 feet or more long. They have successfully invaded virtually every known aquatic habitat. Very few are dangerous to man, although the marine barricuda, the electric fishes, and the vicious piranha of certain South American rivers are exceptions. Many marine and fresh-water forms are edible, and the economy of some countries is based largely on their fishing industries. In most years, some 10 million tons of fish are taken from the waters of the world.

The Amphibians (Class AMPHIBIA, Phylum CHORDATA)

Of the seven vertebrate classes recognized by most zoologists, three are aquatic and three are terrestrial. An intermediate group, the amphibians, have features of both aquatic and terrestrial vertebrates.

Fossil evidence indicates that amphibians arose some 300 million years ago from certain bony fishes in which lungs had evolved. These fishes also had fins which resembled limbs; apparently the animals were adapted to living in conditions of alternate flooding and drying. We know of them today from their fossil remains, and from a very few living species called the **lobe-finned** fishes.

R. H. Noailles

E. P. Haddon; U.S. Fish and Wildlife Service

The most common amphibians are the frogs, toads, and salamanders (Fig. 4.36). Typically, these animals spend their early life stages in water and breathe by means of gills, as the fishes do. Later on they develop lungs and become terrestrial. However, certain salamanders remain aquatic throughout their lives.

The most notable advance over the fishes, at least externally, is the development of legs in the place of fins. Unlike most fishes, amphibians do not have scales. Internally, there are modifications in almost all body systems (Fig. 4.37). In the circulatory system, for example, the two-chambered heart of the fishes is replaced by a three-chambered heart in amphibians. This is a reflection of the greater efficiency required in serving the lungs. Reproduction in this group resembles that of fishes more closely than that of land vertebrates. Amphibians usually lay eggs in open water where they are fertilized and develop into immature forms called **tadpoles.**

Amphibians are of very little value or importance to man. Larger forms are sometimes eaten; legs of the bullfrog, for ex-

W. P. Taylor, U.S. Fish and Wildlife Service

Fig. 4.36 Representative amphibians. Top left: spotted salamander. Top: an albino frog. Above: a toad.

Fig. 4.37 Internal anatomy of a frog. Essentially, this general pattern of structure is characteristic of all vertebrates, although organs may differ among species.

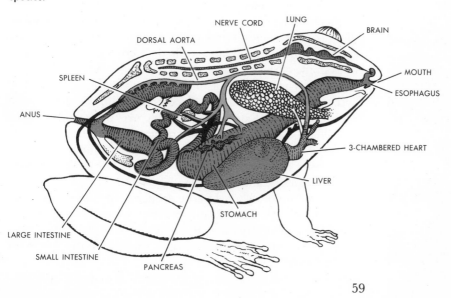

NERVE CORD
LUNG
DORSAL AORTA
BRAIN
SPLEEN
MOUTH
ESOPHAGUS
ANUS
3-CHAMBERED HEART
LIVER
STOMACH
LARGE INTESTINE
SMALL INTESTINE
PANCREAS

Fig. 4.38 Some typical reptiles. Below: a turtle sunning itself on an alligator. Middle: a lizard. Bottom: a female king snake coiled about her eggs.

Leonard Lee Rue III

E. P. Haddon, Fish and Wildlife Service

Leonard Lee Rue III

ample, are considered a delicacy. Toads have long been valued by gardeners because they eat insects, and in some countries, they have been sold for this purpose. No amphibian is dangerous to man in any way. Amphibians are of special interest to the biologist because they are intermediate between the fishes and terrestrial vertebrates. For this and for other reasons, frogs and salamanders are widely used in biological research.

The Reptiles (Class REPTILIA, Phylum CHORDATA)

Among the terrestrial vertebrates we find many adaptations that are related to living on land. For example, the circulatory system is powered by a four-chambered heart. In most reptiles, however, the two upper chambers (called the **atria**) are not completely separated. Another striking difference between terrestrial forms and the fishes and amphibians is their reproductive adaptations. Fertilization of eggs in the land vertebrates takes place inside the body by direct transfer of sperm from male to female. As a rule, egg fertilization is *external* in fishes and amphibians; the female releases her eggs from the body, after which the male deposits sperm upon or near them.

Since the eggs of fishes and amphibians are laid in water, the embryos of these animals have an unlimited source of vital materials such as oxygen and water molecules. They can also rid themselves of waste materials without difficulty. As a result, development is relatively uncomplicated from that standpoint. Through evolution the land vertebrates have developed a means of producing a micro-environment of water not unlike the larger water environment of fishes and amphibians. The land vertebrates have developed a membrane, the **amnion,** which is a sac enclosing the embryo within water. Embryos of reptiles, birds, and mammals all develop within an amnion. An example of this is shown in Fig. 4.39.

The slow-moving habits of most reptiles are well described by the Latin word meaning "to creep," from which the word "reptile" comes. Externally, reptiles are distinguished from amphibians by having scales and digital claws. Internally, there are many differences, as the diagram shows. The reptiles with which most of us are best acquainted are the snakes, lizards, turtles, alligators, and crocodiles (Fig. 4.38).

Reptiles are of relatively little economic importance to man. On the whole, they are simply a group of interesting animals whose place in nature today is not nearly so important as it was 150 million years ago. At that time, they were the dominant vertebrates on earth.

Some species of snakes are extremely poisonous, especially

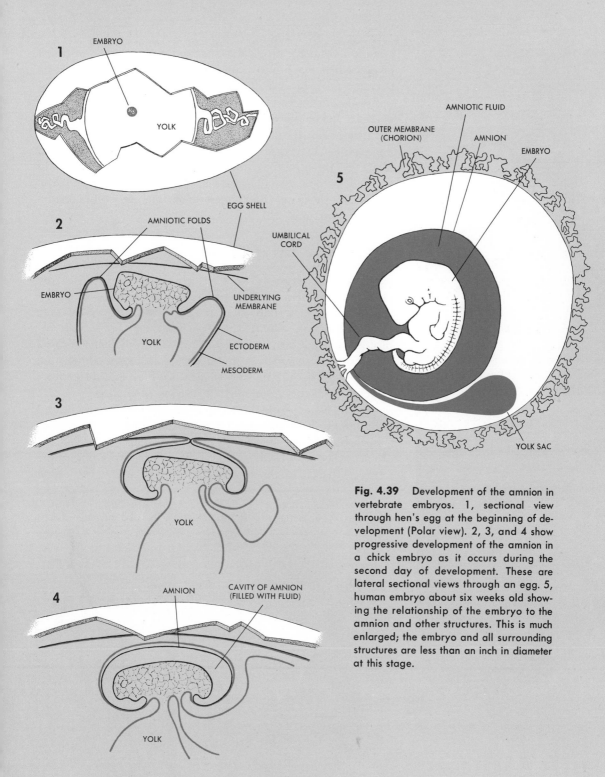

1

EMBRYO

YOLK

EGG SHELL

2

AMNIOTIC FOLDS

EMBRYO

UNDERLYING
MEMBRANE

YOLK

ECTODERM

MESODERM

3

YOLK

4

AMNION

CAVITY OF AMNION
(FILLED WITH FLUID)

YOLK

5

AMNIOTIC FLUID

OUTER MEMBRANE
(CHORION)

AMNION

EMBRYO

UMBILICAL
CORD

YOLK SAC

Fig. 4.39 Development of the amnion in vertebrate embryos. 1, sectional view through hen's egg at the beginning of development (Polar view). 2, 3, and 4 show progressive development of the amnion in a chick embryo as it occurs during the second day of development. These are lateral sectional views through an egg. 5, human embryo about six weeks old showing the relationship of the embryo to the amnion and other structures. This is much enlarged; the embryo and all surrounding structures are less than an inch in diameter at this stage.

certain marine and tropical forms; and in some areas alligators or crocodiles reach a sufficient size and exist in such numbers that they are quite dangerous to man. Only four types of poisonous snakes are found in the United States. These are the copperhead, the cotton mouth, the coral snake, and several species of rattlesnakes. In addition, a poisonous lizard, the Gila (pronounced hē′-la) monster, lives in the deserts of the Southwest. However, these reptiles are not nearly so dangerous as certain poisonous tropical snakes, such as the cobra, the fer-de-lance, and the bushmaster. Furthermore, certain sea-snakes are extremely poisonous.

The Birds (Class AVES, Phylum CHORDATA)

Birds (Fig. 4.40) are feathered bipeds. Only birds have feathers, and they are somewhat unusual in having only one pair of walking appendages. Birds, too, are the only vertebrates having the power of flight as a group (a very few birds, such as the ostrich, cannot fly) and many of their structural features are related to flight. Their bones, for example, are made lighter by having large central cavities, and their breast muscles are highly developed for moving their wings.

Unlike fishes, amphibians, and reptiles, birds keep a fixed body temperature. Because of this ability, birds are said to be "warm-blooded." All other vertebrates (except the mammals) are described as "cold-blooded." Actually, these are misleading terms. A lizard in the desert, for example, whose body tem-

Fig. 4.40 Representative birds. Left: a vulture. This bird is highly valuable as a scavenger. Below, left: a leghorn hen, widely raised as an egg-producer. Right: young green herons.

P. A. Knipping

Standard Oil Co. (N.J.)

Lynwood M. Chace

Fig. 4.41 A comparison of beak structure among various birds. Can you infer the feeding habit in each case?

perature changes with that of the surrounding air, might have a much higher temperature than a mammal living in the same environment.

Because they can fly and maintain a constant body temperature, birds have become a very successful group within the past 100 million years. We have abundant fossil evidence of flying reptiles during the time of the dinosaurs. Birds evidently evolved from such reptilian stock. Feathers and scales, by the way, are produced in much the same fashion in bird and reptile embryos, respectively. Birds still have scales on their legs as one mark of their ancestry.

Except for those modifications related to flight, the internal anatomy of birds is almost identical to that of reptiles. There are few animal groups in which more variety exists. In size, birds range from small forms such as hummingbirds to large ones such as eagles. There are also striking differences in color, wing and tail forms, beak shape, and foot structure. For example, even very closely related birds often have beaks that vary in shape (see Fig. 4.41). This variation results in completely different feeding habits, which in turn may reduce competition for food between these birds to such an extent that they can live in harmony in the same locality (see Darwin's finches, page 24).

The birds are of considerable importance to man. Certain species have been prized as food since prehistoric times. The domestic chicken of our day (developed from the wild fowl of Malay) is an important food source of meat and eggs alike. Various wild birds such as ducks and geese are hunted widely. Birds consume large numbers of harmful insects, thus benefiting the farmer and the gardener. From the recreational and aesthetic viewpoint, birds are very important. Whether or not we are interested enough in birds to join a bird-watching group, most of us enjoy hearing song birds and seeing their bright colors.

Armour and Company

The Mammals (Class MAMMALIA, Phylum CHORDATA)

At a time when reptiles were still the dominant vertebrates, some 150 million years ago, a group of rather small animals developed. They were destined to supersede the giant lizards and develop into the most complex animals of all. These were the mammals (Fig. 4.42). At first, they were no larger than mice or rats, but they were able to maintain a constant body temperature. This plus certain other features which they developed in time (such as a more complex nervous system) enabled them to survive environmental changes which most of the reptiles of that time could not tolerate.

The mammals are those vertebrates which have hair as an external body covering, and which are nourished in their very young stages by milk secreted by the mother. During the millions of years since the mammals first arose, great diversity has taken place. While there are still some very small mammals, such as shrews, the largest animals on Earth also belong to this group. The modern blue whale, for example, is the largest animal ever known to have existed, exceeding even the size of the largest dinosaurs.

Fig. 4.42 As these photographs show, there is great variety among mammals. Top, left: Hereford cattle are a popular breed of animals domesticated by man. Opposite: a pair of jaguars (male black, female spotted). Bottom: a white whale in its water environment. Below: camels in a camel market at Kassala, in the Sudan.

United Nations

© MCMLX Walt Disney Productions
New York Zoological Society Photo

Compared with other vertebrates, the mammals show an advance in complexity and specialization in nearly every system of the body. The superior brain and nervous system of mammals make these animals more "intelligent," as a group, than any other animals. Another superior feature is their mode of reproduction. Almost all the animals we have studied in this chapter are **oviparous;** that is, they produce relatively large eggs which develop outside the body of the mother. With mammals, all except one primitive group are **viviparous;** that is, the females produce eggs which undergo both fertilization and development inside the body of the mother. Incidentally, certain animals produce large oviparous-type eggs which develop and hatch within the mother's body, and the young are thus born alive, as in the viviparous state. The pit vipers, which include the rattlesnake, the copperhead, and the cotton mouth, reproduce in this fashion. Such animals are said to be **ovoviparous.**

As in other successful animal groups we have studied, there is wide variety among the mammals. We have already seen the extremes in size. In adaptation, the variety is even greater. One group, the bats, can fly. Whales and porpoises, although they live in the ocean, are mammals. Most mammals, however, are entirely terrestrial. Altogether, zoologists recognize some 20 different orders, each of which is distinctive in some way. Among the more interesting forms are the **marsupials,** or pouched mammals (for example, the opossum and the kangaroo), the **primates** (monkeys and their kin), the elephants, the carnivores, and the various **ungulates** (hoofed mammals).

Man is more dependent directly upon other mammals than upon any other animal group. We do not know when men began domesticating such animals as the dog, the horse, and the cow, but it was long before history began to be recorded. It is a curious fact that no additional important animals have been domesticated by man within the past 5,000 years or so. Although such work animals as the horse are not as important to our present mechanized society as they were only a few decades ago, we still use them to a great extent. The mammals upon which we depend for food are of greatest importance. Milk, cheese, beef, pork, and mutton are a few of the more important mammalian products. In addition, mammals furnish us with such materials as leather and wool; even the manure of domesticated mammals is put to good use as fertilizer. To cite an entirely different sort of value, man's favorite pets are mammals. There is good evidence that the dog was the first domesticated animal (whether for companionship or for assistance in hunting, we do not know), and it has remained a popular pet.

Before we end our brief survey of mammals, let us consider

Courtesy of The American Museum of Natural History

Fig. 4.43 These reconstructions of three humans, or near-humans, who lived in the past are based on anatomical studies of fossilized skeletons. Top: Cro-Magnon man, who lived about 50,000 years ago. Middle: Java man, who existed perhaps 500,000 years ago. Above: Neanderthal man, who is thought to have occupied southern Europe more than 100,000 years ago.

the order Primates, of which man is a member. This order also includes the monkeys and apes as well as a variety of forms that are less familiar to most people (tree shrews, lemurs, galagos, tarsiers, marmosets, and so on).

Fossil and other evidence indicates that the primates arose at least 70 million years ago from mammalian ancestors that were **insectivores** (insect eaters), much like modern shrews and moles. At first, the primates were relatively small animals (many still are) and the larger forms did not evolve until several million years later. The best evidence indicates that man himself arose from a primate stock which at least 25 million years ago separated from the evolutionary lines that produced other living primates. This stock gave rise to a number of pre-men, or near-men, sometimes called "ape-men," whose fossil remains (Fig. 4.43) have been studied. The most primitive of these primates were still living at least a million years ago. By 500,000 years ago, several more advanced forms had evolved. All species of this evolutionary line are now extinct except modern man, *Homo sapiens,* who arose at least 100,000 years ago.

THE EVOLUTION OF ANIMALS

Fossil remains do not always give us a clear picture of what happened in the past, although they do tell us that evolution occurred. In many cases, we must turn to the fields of biochemistry, embryology, and anatomy (Fig. 4-44) to supplement the fossil evidence.

How can we make a general statement about the way evolution has taken place? We might arrange the phyla we have discussed in order from the Protozoa to the Chordata, and say that protozoans gave rise to sponges, sponges gave rise to cnidarians, etc. But this (see Fig. 4.45) would be wrong—just the same as saying that present-day forms have arisen from other present-day forms. This pattern, we are sure, is not reasonable in the light of our evidence. Rather, we must visualize evolution as a branching tree (Fig. 4.45), many of whose lower limbs have become lost through extinction and replacement.

In other words, the common ancestors of many present-day groups probably bore very little resemblance to any modern animals. (See Fig. 4.46 for a simplified and very generalized illustration of this evolutionary pattern.) It should be pointed out that this "tree" has been shorn of its smaller branches, many of which would illustrate groups that have become extinct. Furthermore, within a given group (such as the mammals), we can construct a tree showing the evolution of orders and families.

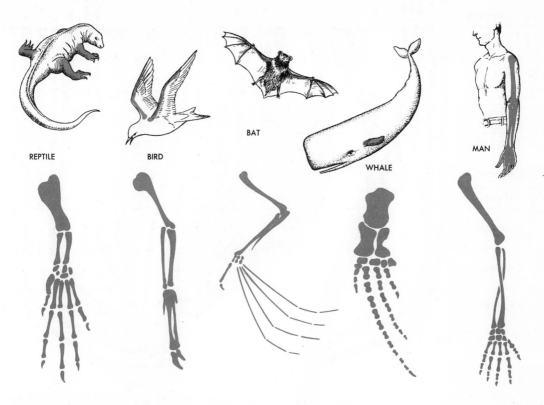

REPTILE BIRD BAT WHALE MAN

Fig. 4.44 In spite of great diversity in both structure and function, the forelimbs of all vertebrates show striking similarities in bone structure. For instance, an upper bone (humerus) is present in each type of limb shown. Such bones as the humerus of a reptile and that of a bat are said to be *homologous*. The study of homology has contributed much to our knowledge of vertebrate evolution.

Fig. 4.45 We cannot arrange present-day organisms in an order of increasing complexity and say that this is how evolution occurred. The course of evolution is more like a branching tree than a straight line.

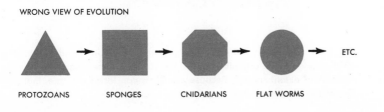

WRONG VIEW OF EVOLUTION

PROTOZOANS SPONGES CNIDARIANS FLAT WORMS ETC.

RIGHT VIEW OF EVOLUTION

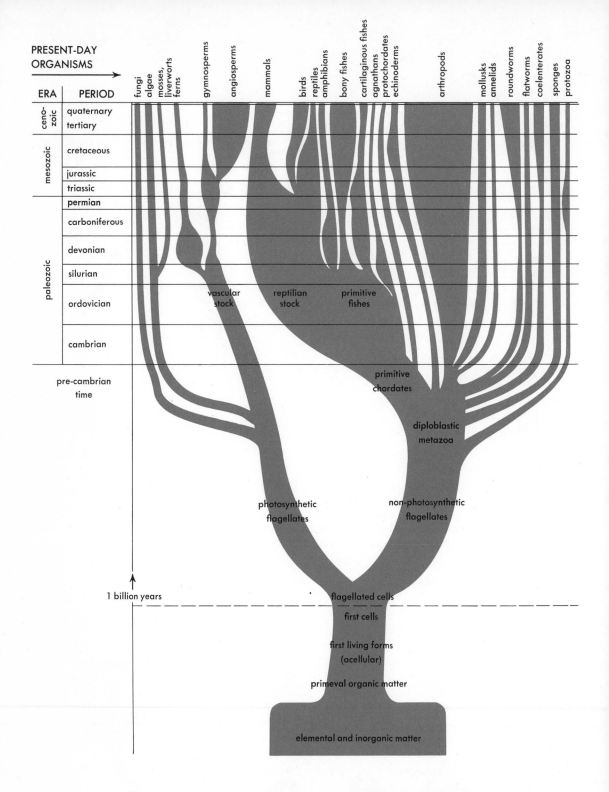

Fig. 4.46 The course of evolution, showing the periods and eras during which many modern organisms arose and showing something of the relative numbers of extant species. Because pre-Cambrian fossils are rare, that portion of this diagram is built largely upon inference.

68

Of the origins of animals, we know very little. In rock formations where we might expect to find the answers to our questions, the stresses of time have been too great for many fossil forms to be preserved. The first time period from which we find recognizable fossils in abundance is relatively late. It is later than the age in which all the major phyla of the present day evolved. The time chart shows this to have occurred by the beginning of the Cambrian Period, about 570 million years ago. However, it appears probable that the ancestors of animals were flagellates, and that a nonphotosynthetic line gave rise to protozoans and to the ancestors of metazoans. There is some evidence that the metazoan forms which gave rise to most phyla were very similar to the modern free-living flatworms. However, after we put aside these and certain other rather speculative ideas, evolution within the various phyla becomes more clearly illustrated.

As to the kinds of animals that were present on Earth at any given time since the beginning of the Cambrian Period, we have a reasonably clear picture. Up to the Silurian Period, which began about 435 million years ago, the most abundant animals were invertebrates, particularly certain arthropods, mollusks, and echinoderms. Fishes became numerous during the Silurian Period and began to dominate the seas. Animals apparently invaded the land during the Devonian Period, which began some 395 million years ago. These animals included the amphibians, which arose shortly before or during this time, and certain arthropods. The reptiles arose during the Mississippian Period, which began about 345 million years ago. They did not come into their own as the dominant animal group until the Mesozoic Era, which began some 225 million years ago. Small mammals appeared during this time, but they did not replace the reptiles until nearly the end of this era. In the Cenozoic Era, however, which began about 65 million years ago and continues to the present, mammalian evolution has proceeded very rapidly.

SUMMARY

We have considered as major forms 19 animal groups representing 10 phyla (see Table 4-2). The first of these, the protozoans, are unicellular. All other animals are multicellular. The sponges are little more than colonies of protozoan-like cells, and the cnidarians are the simplest animals with tissue specialization. Beginning with the flatworms, the other animals we have discussed are bilaterally symmetrical, with the exception of adult echinoderms. All animals above the flatworm level of

TABLE 4-2. A Listing of the Most Common and Numerous Animal Groups

Common Name	Phylum	Taxonomic Category	Approximate Number of Known Species
Protozoans	Protozoa	Phylum Protozoa	30,000
Sponges	Parazoa	Phylum Parazoa	4,200
Cnidarians or Coelenterates	Cnidaria	Phylum Cnidaria	9,600
Flatworms	Platyhelminthes	Phylum Platyhelminthes	15,000
Nematodes or Roundworms	Aschelminthes	Class Nematoda	10,000
Mollusks	Mollusca	Phylum Mollusca	100,000
Annelids or Segmented Worms	Annelida	Phylum Annelida	7,000
Insects	Arthropoda	Class Insecta	700,000
Crustaceans	Arthropoda	Class Crustacea	25,000
Arachnids	Arthropoda	Class Arachnida	30,000
Centipedes	Arthropoda	Class Chilopoda	3,000
Millipedes	Arthropoda	Class Diplopoda	6,000
Echinoderms	Echinodermata	Phylum Echinodermata	5,700
Protochordates	Chordata	Classes Urochordata, Cephalochordata	1,700
Fishes	Chordata	Classes Agnatha, Chondrichthyes, Osteichthyes	23,000
Amphibians	Chordata	Class Amphibia	2,000
Reptiles	Chordata	Class Reptilia	5,000
Birds	Chordata	Class Aves	8,590
Mammals	Chordata	Class Mammalia	4,500
		Approximate total:	990,000

Adapted from Lord Rothschild, A Classification of Living Animals. By permission, John Wiley and Sons, Inc.

complexity have a body through which a digestive tube runs from mouth to anus. Our consideration and description of the nematodes, mollusks, annelids, five groups of arthropods, echinoderms, and protochordates completes the survey of invertebrate animals. There are five groups of vertebrates—fishes (including three taxonomic classes), amphibians, reptiles, birds, and mammals.

Animal life became distinct from plant life approximately a billion years ago. Metazoan animals arose and evolved into the major present-day phyla some time before the Cambrian Period, which began about 570 million years ago. Since that time, great diversity has occurred, with different groups succeeding each other as the dominant animals. The land was invaded by animal life some 395 million years ago, and within 150 million years, reptiles had evolved and had become the dominant terrestrial vertebrates. They were replaced in this role by the mammals after approximately 100 million years.

FOR THOUGHT AND DISCUSSION

1 What three phyla include nine-tenths of all animals that have been classified? Which of these three phyla is the largest? What *group* of this phylum includes more animals than any other?

2 Why are the echinoderms placed where they are in the evolutionary scale, since they resemble animals that are ranked much lower?

3 Only two groups of animals, as groups, are characterized by flight. Which are they? Can you think of any animals outside these groups that can fly?

4 What is the distinction between protochordates and vertebrates?

5 Which of the animal groups that we have discussed do you consider to be of major economic importance to man? Make a list and give reasons.

6 The reptiles, birds, and mammals are sometimes called the **Amniota.** What do you suppose gave rise to this name, and of what significance is it?

7 What is regeneration? It is exhibited to a greater degree in less complex animals and to a lesser degree in more complex animals. Can you propose a reasonable explanation for this?

8 Will taxonomists ever reach a stopping point in their classification of animals? Justify your answer.

SELECTED READINGS

Blair, W. F., A. P. Blair, P. Brodkorb, F. R. Cagle, and G. A. Moore. *Vertebrates of the United States.* New York: McGraw-Hill Book Co., Inc., 1957.

This book is essentially a taxonomic work, and is somewhat specialized. It gives a description of each of the thousands of vertebrates found in the United States.

Buchsbaum, R. *Animals Without Backbones* (2nd ed.). Chicago: The University of Chicago Press, 1948.

A classic of descriptive invertebrate zoology, this book is beautifully written and illustrated.

Hanson, E. D. *Animal Diversity* (2nd ed.). Englewood Cliffs, N.J.: Prentice-Hall, Inc., 1964.

The viewpoint of this book is evolutionary, rather than descriptive. It is a stimulating discussion of this aspect of zoology.

Storer, T. I. and R. L. Usinger. *General Zoology* (4th ed.). New York: McGraw-Hill Book Co., Inc., 1965.

A thorough presentation of the animal kingdom.

5 THE PLANT KINGDOM

Fig. 5.1 The majestic redwood trees of the west coast may attain an age of thousands of years.

David Swanlund, Save-the-Redwoods League

Grasses, trees, mosses, hedges, and various small flowering plants—how many other kinds of plants can you add to this list? Probably not very many, for these five make up the bulk of terrestrial vegetation. Nevertheless, there are many other kinds of plants.

Virtually all of the plants we see around us are green plants. As you probably know, **chlorophyll** is the substance that makes green plants green. In the presence of sunlight and chlorophyll, water and carbon dioxide within a plant unite and form carbohydrates, releasing oxygen during the process. This is called **photosynthesis.** The oxygen we breathe is made by the action of green plants.

You might think that the green plants mentioned at the beginning of the chapter supply all, or nearly all, of the free oxygen we breathe, but they do not. The greater part, probably more than 80 per cent, of photosynthesis is carried on, not by terrestrial plants, like the giant redwoods of Fig. 5.1, but by small and relatively simple aquatic plants called algae, whose very existence is unknown to many people. The fact that these plants are so important in the over-all economy of nature is an indication of our need to know more about them. This is only one example of the many plant groups that are important to us, and of which most people know very little.

How Plants Are Classified

Although it seems incredible to us now, there was a time when students of **botany** (the study of plants) recognized only a few hundred plant species. Aristotle's student, Theophrastus, for example, classified about 500 plants. Linnaeus, some 2,000 years later, listed fewer than 10,000 species. As you saw in the first chapter, today we recognize about 350,000 species. However, we should remember that travel was difficult

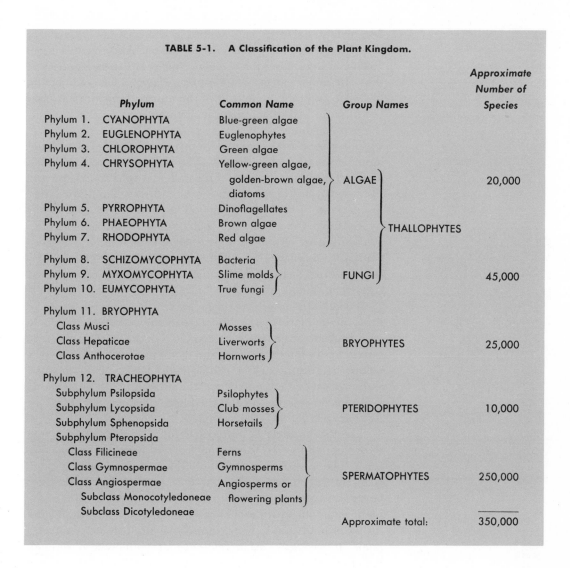

TABLE 5-1.   A Classification of the Plant Kingdom.

Phylum	Common Name	Group Names	Approximate Number of Species
Phylum 1. CYANOPHYTA	Blue-green algae		
Phylum 2. EUGLENOPHYTA	Euglenophytes		
Phylum 3. CHLOROPHYTA	Green algae		
Phylum 4. CHRYSOPHYTA	Yellow-green algae, golden-brown algae, diatoms	ALGAE	20,000
Phylum 5. PYRROPHYTA	Dinoflagellates		
Phylum 6. PHAEOPHYTA	Brown algae	THALLOPHYTES	
Phylum 7. RHODOPHYTA	Red algae		
Phylum 8. SCHIZOMYCOPHYTA	Bacteria		
Phylum 9. MYXOMYCOPHYTA	Slime molds	FUNGI	45,000
Phylum 10. EUMYCOPHYTA	True fungi		
Phylum 11. BRYOPHYTA			
Class Musci	Mosses		
Class Hepaticae	Liverworts	BRYOPHYTES	25,000
Class Anthocerotae	Hornworts		
Phylum 12. TRACHEOPHYTA			
Subphylum Psilopsida	Psilophytes		
Subphylum Lycopsida	Club mosses	PTERIDOPHYTES	10,000
Subphylum Sphenopsida	Horsetails		
Subphylum Pteropsida			
Class Filicineae	Ferns		
Class Gymnospermae	Gymnosperms	SPERMATOPHYTES	250,000
Class Angiospermae	Angiosperms or flowering plants		
Subclass Monocotyledoneae			
Subclass Dicotyledoneae			
		Approximate total:	350,000

in the 1700's, to say nothing of travel conditions in ancient Greece. This handicap severely limited the scope of plant investigation.

Linnaeus recognized 24 classes of plants, 23 of which included the flowering plants. Within these classes, he included orders on the basis of differences in structures related to sexual reproduction. For example, he lumped all of the plants that do not bear flowers into one class. Within a very short time his system could not accomodate the many newly-discovered species of both flowering and nonflowering plants.

Various systems succeeded each other until the late 1800's. By this time well over 100,000 species of plants were known.

Meanwhile, botanists had created a category one step above the class, which they called the **division.** Also, by this time, zoologists were using the category "phylum" at the same level; thus, the major category of the plant kingdom has traditionally been the division, while that of the animal kingdom has been the phylum. All other taxonomic categories are the same for the two kingdoms.

One system that employed four divisions of the plant kingdom became widely adopted. The divisions were as follows: 1. Thallophyta (algae and fungi), 2. Bryophyta (mosses and liverworts), 3. Pteridophyta (ferns and fern-like plants), and 4. Spermatophyta (seed plants). This system was used widely by botanists from the late 1800's until recent decades. But as the number of known plant species increased, and as more emphasis was placed on evolutionary principles, the four-divisional system became inadequate. It failed to reflect *natural relationships* among plants.

Several attempts have been made within recent years to draw up a more meaningful classification system, especially with respect to the larger categories. Unfortunately, no single system has become standard, and it will probably be some years before botanists reach a general agreement. This unhappy situation is caused partly by the difficulty of interpreting evolutionary relationships in the plant kingdom; also, evidence for these relationships is incomplete.

The most widely accepted scheme of classification is that shown in Table 5-1. According to this listing, 12 phyla are used. The use of the term "phylum" instead of "division" is interesting in view of what was said earlier. It shows a tendency among botanists to equate the major groups of the plant kingdom with those of the animal kingdom. Although a listing of plant phyla will probably mean little to you at this point, it will serve as a reference as you proceed through the chapter.

A SURVEY OF MAJOR PLANT TYPES

The Algae

Have you ever noticed that ponds often have a greenish appearance? Or, perhaps you have seen the bluish-green scum left on a patch of ground that was covered by a rain puddle. If you were to examine either the pond water or the scum with a microscope, you would see many extremely small plants. Some of them would be only single cells. Although not all algae are microscopic, most of them are much simpler in structure than the more familiar plants. It is because of their structural simplicity that we begin our survey of the plant kingdom with the algae (Fig. 5.2), which are thought to have inhabited the Earth one-and-a-half billion years ago.

As you will notice in Table 5-1 the group is quite varied, consisting of seven phyla. In addition to the microscopic, one-celled individuals, there are the marine kelps, of the brown algae, which can grow to 100 feet in length, and are very complex in structure. In general, however, the algae are rather small plants. Some phyla consist entirely of microscopic forms.

Algae have the green pigment, chlorophyll. They are widely distributed in nature, especially in marine or fresh-water habitats. However, many species are terrestrial. They live in hot springs, where the water temperature may be 85°C, in the melted water of snowbanks, in deserts, and in the polar regions. Some grow on rocks, wood, or in association with other types of plants, or with animals. You can often see excellent cultures of algae growing on the shells of turtles. There seems to be hardly any terrestrial environment to which the algae have not successfully adapted.

Although it is difficult to make a clear-cut distinction between the algae and other groups of plants, the major difference is one of complexity in form and structure, especially in the organs of sexual reproduction. Very few algae have parts that resemble roots, stem, leaves, or other organs of higher green plants. Let us now examine some of the more important types of algae.

Fig. 5.2   The pond scum which the girl is examining consists of thousands of filaments of green algae. When viewed under a microscope, individual plants making up this scum are strikingly beautiful.

The Blue-green Algae (Phylum CYANOPHYTA)

Members of this phylum have certain red and blue pigments which, in addition to chlorophyll, give them the color their name implies. Some occur as free-living individual cells while others form thread-like structures called **filaments** (Fig. 5.4). Unlike the vast majority of plant and animal cells, which have well-formed nuclei, the blue-green algae have cells in which the DNA is not contained within an inner confining membrane, or definite nucleus.

Also unlike most other organisms (Fig. 5.3), they do not reproduce sexually. New algae are produced by cell divisions of old individuals. A cell simply "pinches" itself into two hemispheres until it divides; each new cell shares parts of the loose nuclear material and the cell fluid, called **cytoplasm.** This method of cell division is much less precise than that shown by most plant cells (Fig. 5.3). For these and certain other reasons, the blue-green algae are among the least complex of all living organisms.

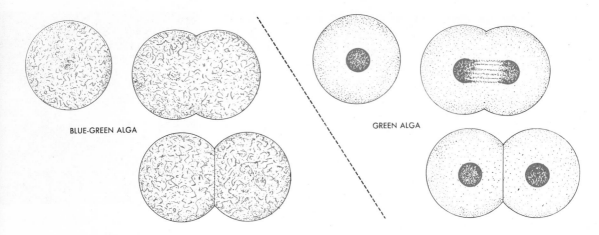

BLUE-GREEN ALGA

GREEN ALGA

Fig. 5.3 Cells of blue-green algae (left, above) do not undergo precise nuclear division. Virtually all other cells show a process of nuclear division (called **mitosis**), exemplified at right by cell division in a green alga. (See left-hand portion of Fig. 5.10 for a detailed diagram of mitotic division.)

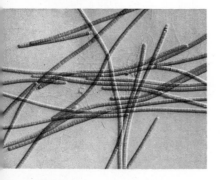

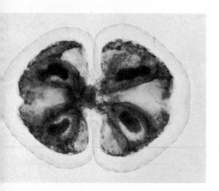

Fig. 5.4 Top photo: filaments of *Oscillatoria,* a blue-green alga. Above: *Cosmarium,* a single-celled green alga.

The Green Algae (Phylum CHLOROPHYTA)

These plants are the most varied, numerous, and widespread of all the algae. They are generally grass-green because chlorophyll is their major pigment. Like the blue-green algae, they live as unicellular forms and in filamentous colonies which frequently grow in such abundance in ponds or ditches that they appear as a frothy mass or scum.

The cells of green algae are much more highly organized than those of blue-green algae. They have definite nuclei and other specialized parts characteristic of higher plants. For instance, the pigment chlorophyll is contained in definite bodies called **chloroplasts** in the green algae and in higher green plants. In contrast, the pigments found in the cells of blue-green algae are diffused throughout the cell. The chloroplasts of green algae contain bodies called **pyrenoids,** which are storage centers for starch made during photosynthesis. Also characteristic of higher plants, the cells of green algae have walls composed chiefly of the carbohydrate cellulose.

Sexual reproduction, during which two gametes unite and form a zygote, as we saw in the animal kingdom chapter, is also characteristic of higher plants and is widespread among species of the green algae. Yet many species reproduce asexually by fission. We shall have more to say about methods of reproduction later.

The Brown Algae (Phylum PHAEOPHYTA)

The dominant pigment in these algae is brown, hence their common name. Although chlorophyll is present, it is heavily masked in most species of this phylum. The cellular characteristics of brown algae are much like those of the green algae, and sexual reproduction is carried on by virtually all species. Most brown algae are relatively large and complex (Fig. 5.5).

There are no unicellular, or even very small forms. A single giant kelp ("seaweed") of the Pacific may have a total mass equal to that of a fairly large tree. The internal structure of these and other large brown algae approaches the complexity of that of many higher plants. A very few fresh water species are known. Most members of the group are marine.

The Red Algae (Phylum RHODOPHYTA)

A reddish pigment that masks the chlorophyll gives members of this phylum their common name. They are graceful forms (Fig. 5.6) that live anchored to the ocean bottom, to rocks, or to floating debris. Although most species are marine, many fresh water forms are known. Several of the red algae are rather complex, especially their sexual reproductive systems. No known member of this phylum reaches the size of the larger brown algae.

What roles do algae play in nature? And of what values are they to man? Indirectly, algae benefit man by playing a vital

Courtesy The Bronx Botanical Garden

Fig. 5.5 *Macrocystis pyrifera,* one of the larger and more complex forms of brown algae known as "kelps." See Fig. 5.11 for a smaller type of brown alga.

Fig. 5.6 *Polysiphonia,* a marine red alga.

Courtesy Carolina Biological Supply House

PHOTOSYNTHETIC PRODUCER
(ALGAE)

PRIMARY CONSUMERS
(SMALL FISHES AND
VARIOUS INVERTEBRATES)

ULTIMATE CONSUMER
(PORPOISE)

DECOMPOSER
(BACTERIA)

Fig. 5.7   This simplified representation of a food web in nature shows the interdependence of living forms. What is the role of sunlight in this complex web, and why is it called a "web?"

role as members of the endless **food web** (Fig. 5.7). On the first level are the photosynthetic **producers**—called "producers" because they build themselves up entirely by using the water, carbon dioxide, and minerals of their immediate environment. On the land, they are chiefly the rooted higher plants; in water, the vast majority are algae.

At the next level of aquatic food are the **primary consumers,** such as the small fishes and various invertebrate animals that consume the algae. In turn, the primary consumers are eaten by still larger animals, and so on, until some **ultimate consumer,** a porpoise, say, ends the process. Even here, however, the ultimate consumer produces waste products and eventually dies. The **decomposers,** such as bacteria, now play their role in the food web.

Consequently, the original energy that was captured by algae or other producers is made available to different organisms. About three-fourths of the Earth's surface is covered by water, and about four-fifths of all photosynthesis is carried on by algae. This means that they are the major producers in the over-all food web.

While man enjoys the indirect effects of algal photosynthesis, he also uses certain algae directly. Some species are edible. At the present time much research is being conducted to explore the possibilities of making the oceans and bodies of fresh water produce algae that can be used directly as food in large quantities. Even now, several types of algae make up a large portion of the diet of certain oriental peoples. Quite a number of valuable chemical substances come from algae. **Agar-agar** (from certain red algae) is useful in laboratories for the preparation of media used in growing microorganisms. **Algin** (from certain brown algae) is used in some food recipes. In addition to these benefits, the microscopic algae in particular have become extremely useful in genetical, nutritional, and biochemical research.

Before leaving the algae, we should describe their methods of reproduction. It is important to do so not only for the sake of understanding the group itself, but for understanding certain basic principles that will apply to the plant groups we will study next.

As we saw earlier, individuals reproduce by sexual or asexual means. Typically, sexual reproduction occurs when a relatively small sperm, or male gamete, unites with a relatively large egg, or female gamete. When this happens, the DNA of each gamete nucleus is brought into close association with that of the other. However, there are exceptions to this general rule of sexual reproduction, and our first example of sexual reproduction in algae is one of these exceptions.

Let us consider the life cycle of *Chlamydomonas eugametos*, a unicellular green alga (Fig. 5.8). Cells of this species are **motile;**

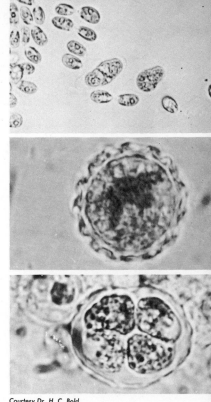

Courtesy Dr. H. C. Bold

Fig. 5.8 Top: cells of *Chlamydomonas eugametos*, some of which are paired in sexual union. Middle: a zygote of *C. eugametos*, much enlarged. Above: meiotic division in the zygote, showing four daughter cells.

Fig. 5.9 Life cycle of *Chlamydomonas eugametos*, sexual phase. Asexual reproduction also occurs whenever individual cells divide.

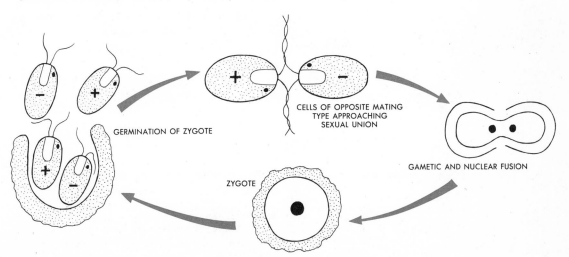

GERMINATION OF ZYGOTE

CELLS OF OPPOSITE MATING TYPE APPROACHING SEXUAL UNION

GAMETIC AND NUCLEAR FUSION

ZYGOTE

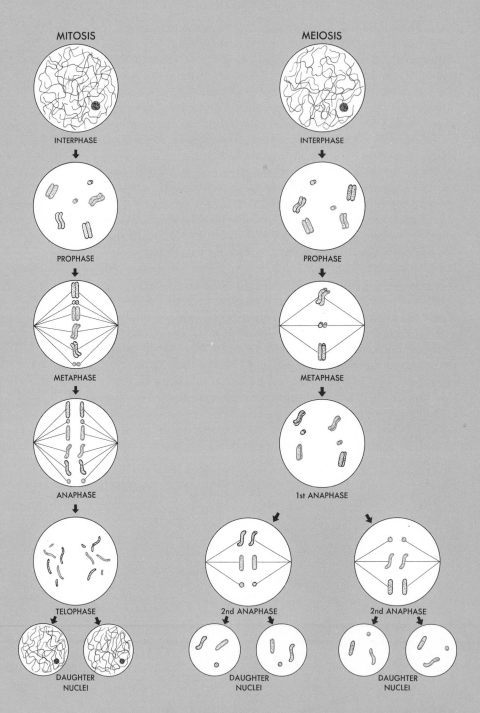

Fig. 5.10   A contrast in mitotic and meiotic nuclear division. In mitosis, each chromosome divides, thus giving each daughter cell exactly the same number of chromosomes as the mother cell. In contrast, meiotic division eventually results in daughter cells that have a chromosome representative of each *pair* present in the mother cell; that is, the number is reduced by one-half. In some way meiosis is always associated with sexual reproduction, and is characteristic of virtually all plants and animals.

that is, they have whip-like **flagella** which propel the cell through water. Although all individuals appear to be similar, by virtue of their behavior they can be assigned to mating groups arbitrarily designated "plus" and "minus." In other words, if there are "male" and "female" groups, we do not know which is which! Under normal conditions, a given cell divides and forms two daughter cells of the same mating type. This particular type of asexual reproduction, called **mitosis,** is shown in its several stages by Fig. 5.10. Each daughter cell is a new individual which may give rise to two new individuals, again by mitosis.

Sometimes, however, two cells of opposite mating type are attracted to each other. Their flagella become entangled, and, after a time, the fluid contents of the two cells mix, and their nuclei unite. The resulting single cell is called a zygote. After a while, the zygote undergoes two successive divisions, called **meiosis,** which produces four cells. Two of these are "plus" and two are "minus" (Figs. 5.9, 5.10).

Thus, *Chlamydomonas eugametos* exhibits both asexual and sexual reproduction. However, sexual reproduction here is somewhat different from that in higher plants and animals. In higher plants and animals, the gametes are individual cells themselves; in *Chlamydomonas* the entire plant, itself only a single cell, serves as a gamete. Furthermore, higher forms usually have gametes of greatly differing size, the egg being many hundreds of times larger than the sperm. In *Chlamydomonas* both gametes are similar in size.

Although the life cycle of *Chlamydomonas* is typical of a great many algae, there are other patterns of reproduction. One of them, shown by the life cycle of *Fucus vesiculosus,* is a more common method of sexual reproduction.

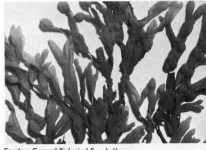

Courtesy General Biological Supply House

Fig. 5.11   *Fucus vesiculosus,* one of the rockweeds (brown algae), shown here slightly smaller than life size.

Fig. 5.12   Life cycle of *Fucus vesiculosus.* 1. mature female plant. If one of the bulb-shaped tips is cut in section, it appears as shown at 2. Groups of eight cells (shown at 3, with only six of the cells visible) are formed and, eventually, produce eight eggs (4). Fertilization occurs in the open sea water when a sperm from a male plant unites with an egg (5). The zygote (6) develops into a mature plant.

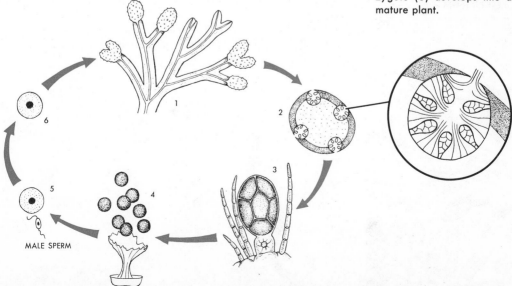

MALE SPERM

Leonard Lee Rue III

This plant (Fig. 5.11), which is found on rocks in tidal areas of the New England coast, reaches sexual maturity when large swellings appear at the tips of the plant. A plant is usually either a male or a female. A female plant produces small clusters of eggs within each swelling; a male plant produces clusters of sperm. Eventually, the sperm and eggs are released. The eggs float passively in the water. The sperm cells, which are motile, are attracted to the eggs. Eventually, one sperm penetrates an egg and fertilization takes place, thus producing a zygote which then develops into a *Fucus* plant. This is shown in diagram form in Fig. 5.12.

The Fungi

Although these plants are widespread in nature, most people are unfamiliar with them as a group. Mushrooms (Fig. 5.13) and certain molds and mildews are quite common members of the group, but there are many other kinds of fungi. Few people are aware of the very important role these plants play. Unlike virtually all other plants, fungi do not have chlorophyll. This sets the fungi apart in appearance from green plants; it also dictates a mode of nutrition which makes the fungi unique as a group. Almost all forms are heterotrophic, which means that their role in nature is one of decomposition.

For our present purposes, we shall include among the fungi two groups of plants that many botanists classify separately— the bacteria and the slime molds.

Lynwood M. Chace

Fig. 5.13 Mushrooms are among the many different kinds of fungi. Other fungi are usually less familiar and less obvious in nature; almost all forms are important as decomposers.

The Bacteria (Phylum SCHIZOMYCOPHYTA)

Most bacteria are unicellular plants, and all of them are extremely small. If 50,000 typical bacteria were laid side by side, they would form a line only about an inch long.

Fig. 5.14 Some representative bacteria, magnified here more than 1,000 times. Left: typical bacilli. Middle: a large spirillum. Right: the cocci which cause pneumonia.

G. J. Hageage G. J. Hageage Courtesy General Biological Supply House

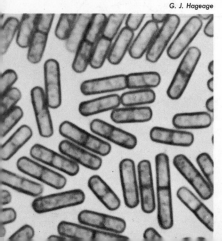

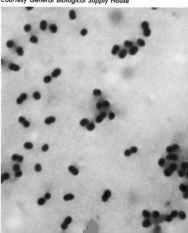

Like the cells of blue-green algae, bacteria have rather poorly organized nuclear material. This is one characteristic that distinguishes them from other fungi. Most bacteria exist as small, unicellular spheres (**cocci**), rods (**bacilli**), or spirals (**spirilla**) as shown in Fig. 5.14.

A few bacteria are **autotrophic** in their nutrition. These autotrophic forms have either certain photosynthetic pigments related to chlorophyll, or they have special mechanisms enabling them to derive energy through chemical reactions with their immediate environment. A few species are parasitic, deriving their food materials from living tissues of higher plants, or animals. If these bacteria cause disease in their host, they are said to be **pathogenic.** Typhoid fever, pneumonia, and tuberculosis are diseases produced by pathogenic bacteria.

The relatively few pathogenic bacteria have given other bacteria a bad name. Most people are surprised to learn that these organisms, as a group, do far more good in nature than harm. They exist in the untold billions in soil, water, and virtually every other medium that exists on the surface of our planet. They maintain their populations by decomposing the remains of other organisms and their products. Sometimes they attack other living organisms. Some bacterial products of metabolism are important in medicine, industry, and agriculture. Certain antibiotics and organic acids, for example, come from cultures of bacteria grown in laboratories. Such bacterial products as ammonia and nitrates, produced in the soil, are of great agricultural importance.

Courtesy A. C. Lonert

Fig. 5.15 A slime mold growing in a laboratory dish, shown here about one-half natural size.

The Slime Molds (Phylum MYXOMYCOPHYTA)

In one stage of their life cycle these plants are so much like animals that they are frequently classified in the animal kingdom. During this stage, a given species exists as a **plasmodium** (Fig. 5.15)—a multinucleate mass of protoplasm that is not divided into cells. A plasmodium, which may be several square feet in area, is capable of moving over the ground. As it travels, it consumes bacteria and bits of debris in true phagotrophic fashion. Eventually, however, the entire mass comes to rest (often on a decaying log) and forms **spore**-producing structures. Spores are reproductive structures consisting of one to several cells, and are characteristic of a great many plants. In most cases, they give rise directly or indirectly to a new plant body like the one which produced them. However, the spores of slime molds develop into gametes. When these gametes are released, two of them may fuse, thus forming a new plasmodium.

Courtesy General Biological Supply House

Fig. 5.16 A mycelium of a mold, *Penicillium*. Grown in culture for its production of the antibiotic penicillin, this mold is an ascomycete (sac fungus), not an algal fungus. It is shown here to illustrate the appearance of a typical mold mycelium. For a representative algal fungus, see Fig. 5.20.

The True Fungi (Phylum EUMYCOPHYTA)

Both the bacteria and the slime molds bear a somewhat obscure evolutionary relationship to those plants which are unquestionably fungi, some of which are discussed below. For this reason, the phylum Eumycophyta ("true fungi") is made to include all fungi other than the bacteria and slime molds. The three most important groups within the Eumycophyta are the algal fungi, the sac fungi, and the club fungi.

The **algal fungi** form a group that includes several common molds, such as the fuzzy mold you sometimes see on bread, cheese, or on the surface of preserves that have been standing about for a long time. Like certain other fungi, the algal fungi form filamentous masses called **mycelia** (Fig. 5.16). But unlike other fungi, the filaments of algal fungi are not divided into cells by cross walls. The algal fungi were given their common name because they resemble certain filamentous algae.

Fig. 5.17 This view of a sac fungus shows ascus (sac) formations, the oval structures near the outer edge.

Courtesy Carolina Biological Supply House

Fig. 5.18 The dead trees shown here were killed by parasitic fungi. After they have died, trees are usually attacked by a variety of decomposing fungi.

Courtesy of The U.S. Forest Service

Like the cells of blue-green algae, bacteria have rather poorly organized nuclear material. This is one characteristic that distinguishes them from other fungi. Most bacteria exist as small, unicellular spheres (**cocci**), rods (**bacilli**), or spirals (**spirilla**) as shown in Fig. 5.14.

A few bacteria are **autotrophic** in their nutrition. These autotrophic forms have either certain photosynthetic pigments related to chlorophyll, or they have special mechanisms enabling them to derive energy through chemical reactions with their immediate environment. A few species are parasitic, deriving their food materials from living tissues of higher plants, or animals. If these bacteria cause disease in their host, they are said to be **pathogenic.** Typhoid fever, pneumonia, and tuberculosis are diseases produced by pathogenic bacteria.

The relatively few pathogenic bacteria have given other bacteria a bad name. Most people are surprised to learn that these organisms, as a group, do far more good in nature than harm. They exist in the untold billions in soil, water, and virtually every other medium that exists on the surface of our planet. They maintain their populations by decomposing the remains of other organisms and their products. Sometimes they attack other living organisms. Some bacterial products of metabolism are important in medicine, industry, and agriculture. Certain antibiotics and organic acids, for example, come from cultures of bacteria grown in laboratories. Such bacterial products as ammonia and nitrates, produced in the soil, are of great agricultural importance.

Courtesy A. C. Lonert

Fig. 5.15 A slime mold growing in a laboratory dish, shown here about one-half natural size.

The Slime Molds (Phylum MYXOMYCOPHYTA)

In one stage of their life cycle these plants are so much like animals that they are frequently classified in the animal kingdom. During this stage, a given species exists as a **plasmodium** (Fig. 5.15)—a multinucleate mass of protoplasm that is not divided into cells. A plasmodium, which may be several square feet in area, is capable of moving over the ground. As it travels, it consumes bacteria and bits of debris in true phagotrophic fashion. Eventually, however, the entire mass comes to rest (often on a decaying log) and forms **spore**-producing structures. Spores are reproductive structures consisting of one to several cells, and are characteristic of a great many plants. In most cases, they give rise directly or indirectly to a new plant body like the one which produced them. However, the spores of slime molds develop into gametes. When these gametes are released, two of them may fuse, thus forming a new plasmodium.

Fig. 5.16 A mycelium of a mold, *Penicillium*. Grown in culture for its production of the antibiotic penicillin, this mold is an ascomycete (sac fungus), not an algal fungus. It is shown here to illustrate the appearance of a typical mold mycelium. For a representative algal fungus, see Fig. 5.20.

Courtesy General Biological Supply House

The True Fungi (Phylum EUMYCOPHYTA)

Both the bacteria and the slime molds bear a somewhat obscure evolutionary relationship to those plants which are unquestionably fungi, some of which are discussed below. For this reason, the phylum Eumycophyta ("true fungi") is made to include all fungi other than the bacteria and slime molds. The three most important groups within the Eumycophyta are the algal fungi, the sac fungi, and the club fungi.

The **algal fungi** form a group that includes several common molds, such as the fuzzy mold you sometimes see on bread, cheese, or on the surface of preserves that have been standing about for a long time. Like certain other fungi, the algal fungi form filamentous masses called **mycelia** (Fig. 5.16). But unlike other fungi, the filaments of algal fungi are not divided into cells by cross walls. The algal fungi were given their common name because they resemble certain filamentous algae.

Fig. 5.17 This view of a sac fungus shows ascus (sac) formations, the oval structures near the outer edge.

Courtesy Carolina Biological Supply House

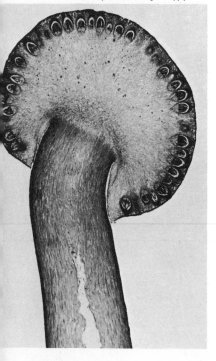

Fig. 5.18 The dead trees shown here were killed by parasitic fungi. After they have died, trees are usually attacked by a variety of decomposing fungi.

Courtesy of The U.S. Forest Service

The **sac fungi** (Fig. 5.17) got their name because they bear their spores within a sac-like enclosure, the **ascus.** The major common types are the **yeasts,** several **molds,** the **mildews,** and fleshy forms known as **cup fungi.**

The yeasts have become extremely valuable to man because of their ability to produce alcohol and carbon dioxide, which makes them particularly important to the beverage and baking industries. Furthermore, yeasts are an important source of the B vitamins, and are either processed into medicines or food, or consumed directly for their nutritive value by humans and livestock. Several molds of this group have come into prominence within recent years because they are capable of producing important drugs. The antibiotic penicillin is produced by a blue-green mold. Certain molds are also valuable in biological research. Study of the pink mold *Neurospora* has led to discovery of some of the fundamental principles of genetics and biochemistry.

The **club fungi** received their common name because they produce spores on club-like structures, known as **basidia.** As a group, they are probably more familiar to most people than any other fungi. Some of the major types are the **rusts** and **smuts.** They are parasites that attack higher plants, particularly cereal grains such as corn and wheat.

The rusts and smuts are of considerable economic importance. They often seriously damage their host plants, thus reducing yield to the farmer. Although parasitic **shelf fungi** may damage timber, most of them and their near relatives, including the **puffballs** (Fig. 5.19) and **mushrooms** (Fig. 5.13), are important decomposers. In this capacity they are beneficial to man. Many types of fungi, including club fungi, grow on both living and dead trees (Fig. 5.18). A few species, including certain mushrooms, are edible and can be grown as a marketable food item.

As we have seen from this short survey, the fungi show remarkable diversity in form. They range in size and complexity from the unicellular bacteria to the larger club fungi. Compared with many of the higher plants, and even with the larger algae, they are all relatively small and simple in structure. Even the mushrooms are essentially masses of interwoven filaments. Only those cells controlling reproduction show much specialization. Like the algae, very few fungi have structures resembling the roots, stems, or leaves of higher plants.

Almost all species of fungi reproduce sexually, but their life cycles vary a great deal. At the simplest level, some bacteria are known to carry on a form of sexual reproduction. At the other end of the spectrum, some parasitic fungi (rusts) have extremely complicated life cycles. The reproductive cycles of

Fig. 5.19 *Geaster,* the earth star, a common puffball.

Courtesy Carolina Biological Supply House

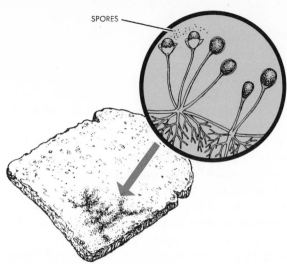

SPORES

Fig. 5.20 *Rhizopus*, the black bread mold, is an algal fungus. In the photograph shown at the left, a single stalk with its anchoring filaments is shown enlarged many times. The knob on the end of the stalk is the sporangium, in which hundreds of spores are produced. The drawing above shows the relationship between the filaments (which compose a mycelium) to the material upon which they grow.

most fungi are somewhat intermediate between these extremes; *Rhizopus,* the bread mold pictured in Fig. 5.20, is a good example. Filaments that originate from a single spore are either "plus" or "minus." If plus and minus strains are grown close together, their filaments fuse at various points and form spiny zygotes. Each zygote has several pairs of fused nuclei (zygote nuclei). Only one nucleus within a zygote, however, eventually germinates and begins a new growth of filaments.

Many fleshy fungi, such as the mushrooms, have elaborate filamentous growth beneath the soil. After sexual fusion occurs between opposite mating types, the large "fruiting body" (the mushroom itself) appears above the soil.

The greatest importance of fungi is their ability to decompose organic materials. When they do so, elements and compounds are released into the environment to be used again by higher plants and animals. Furthermore, fungi prevent an accumulation of dead bodies, animal wastes, and various other materials that would gather on the surface of the earth. For these and other reasons, the fungi are one of the most important plant groups.

The Lichens

You have probably noticed grey-green patches of growth on rocks and tree trunks, especially on the more shaded side. These are **lichens** (Fig. 5.21), a composite of an algal species and a fungal species growing together in a close relation-

Fig. 5.21 A representative lichen growing on a tree limb.

Courtesy Carolina Biological Supply House

86

ship (mutualism). Neither the alga nor the fungus could survive separately under most natural conditions, but the two thrive in biological partnership.

Lichens are very widespread in nature. Frequently they grow where other plants exist only with great difficulty, or not at all. Lichens thrive on the surface of bare rocks, on high mountain peaks, in the Arctic and in deserts alike. They are of little economic importance, although some are processed for dyestuffs or other chemicals, and certain forms are useful in biochemical research. They help break down rocks and so play a part in the formation of soil. They also support animal life in regions where they are virtually the only available vegetation.

Since a given lichen reproduces consistently as a lichen—and not as either an alga or a fungus—it is considered a species in its own right. Hence, the lichens are given generic-specific names in spite of the fact that their algal and fungal components have generic-specific names of their own. This creates an awkward situation taxonomically. All lichens are classified in the phylum Eumycophyta, because the fungal component (a "true fungus") belongs to this group. The algal component is always either green or blue-green.

The Liverworts (Phylum BRYOPHYTA)

These plants are not widespread in nature. Their environments usually are moist, shaded areas. A few are aquatic (fresh water, never marine), but most species grow on soil, where they may form a flat, green carpet. Some, but not all, exhibit a habit of growth that makes individual plants branch out and resemble the lobed human liver. For this reason they have long been known as liverworts (pronounced *wurt,* an old name meaning "plant"). See Fig. 5.22.

Although liverworts are of no economic importance and play a very minor role in nature, they are of tremendous significance to botanists. For one thing, the liverworts have a life cycle (Fig. 5.23) that is typical of all other plants studied in the remainder of this chapter.

The liverwort plant itself consists of cells whose nuclei contain only one set of chromosomes. Any organism in which this condition exists is said to be **haploid.** This term is also applied to any single cell or nucleus, and frequently, the haploid condition is symbolized by the letter **n**. In contrast, the body cells of animals and those of most higher plants contain two sets of chromosomes, and their bodies or cells are said to be **diploid.** The symbol **2n** is used to describe this condition. In the case of liverworts, the specialization of certain cells results in haploid

Fig. 5.22 A typical "carpet" of liverworts, shown here somewhat smaller than natural size. The "heads," which superficially resemble tiny flowers, are reproductive structures. Can you make out the lobes of individual plants?

Courtesy Carolina Biological Supply House

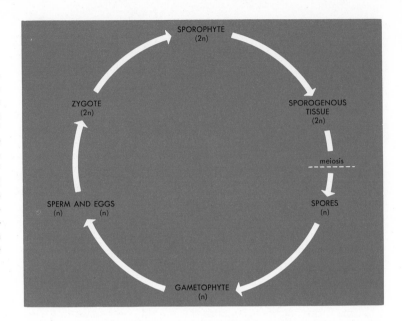

Fig. 5.23 This is a life cycle diagram of plants exhibiting both the gametophyte and the sporophyte stages. The designation "n" means that the cells at that particular stage have a single "set" of chromosomes; "2n" means that cells have paired chromosomes; that is, there are two "sets." Meiosis reduces the chromosome number from 2n to n; fertilization doubles the chromosome number from n to 2n.

eggs and sperm. Zygotes produced by the union of eggs and sperm develop into many-celled, diploid **sporophytes** that lie within the tissues of the liverwort. Eventually, these sporophytes produce cells that undergo meiosis and form haploid **spores.** When these are released from the plant and germinate, they grow into liverwort plants.

The significant thing about the liverwort life cycle is that there are two distinct phases. The plant itself is called a **gametophyte,** because it produces **gametes,** that is, eggs and sperm. Although sporophytes produced by the union of eggs and sperm are not really different plants, their diploid condition makes them a separate **phase** of the life cycle. Hence, the life cycle of liverworts consists of two phases that alternate with each other, the haploid gametophyte and the diploid sporophyte.

With some important variations that we shall note, this type of life cycle is characteristic of the vast majority of plants. This is in contrast to animals, where the gametes are the only haploid cells in the life cycle. Although the gametophyte is the outstanding phase in liverworts, the sporophyte gains in prominence as we proceed up the scale of complexity in the plant kingdom. When we reach the flowering plants, which are the most advanced of all, we find that the sporophyte is the main body of the plant. The gametophyte has been greatly reduced in relative size and importance.

In emphasizing the importance of liverworts as the simplest of a long line of green plants whose life cycles bear a general resemblance to each other, we have not meant to imply that liverworts were the original ancestors of these plants. The fossil record does not indicate that this was the case. In fact, many algae have a sporophyte-gametophyte life cycle of this type, and it is generally supposed that the algae, not liverworts, gave rise to the higher plants, including liverworts. As you saw earlier, the algae have other types of life cycles as well. However, the liverwort type of life cycle has been generally more successful than other types in evolution. As a result, it is characteristic of those plants that are more complex than algae and fungi.

The Mosses (Phylum BRYOPHYTA)

Like liverworts, most mosses (Fig. 5.24) are relatively small plants usually found in moist surroundings. However, mosses are more abundant than liverworts, and, as a group, they require less water. Most mosses are terrestrial, although some forms grow in bogs or marshes, and a few are submerged aquatics. In addition, certain species may grow on wood or rock. The mosses are of limited direct economic value to man, although some are used as packing materials. Peat moss (*Sphagnum*) is widely used by gardeners to increase the acidity and water-holding capacity of soil. The sponge-like quality of mosses has also made them useful in certain types of surgical dressings. Their indirect economic value can be great, since they frequently prevent soil erosion.

Fig. 5.24 The two phases of the moss life cycle: At left is a dense growth of moss gametophytes. At right are several sporophytes, each growing from a gametophyte.

R. H. Noailles   R. H. Noailles

The life cycle of mosses (see Fig. 5.25) is essentially that of liverworts. In both groups the gametophyte is more obvious than the sporophyte. However, the moss sporophyte is far more prominent than that of liverworts. Typically, it is a knobbed stalk borne by the female plant (or a female branch in the case of plants that are bisexual). The physical relationship between the sporophyte (stalk) and gametophyte (leafy plant) is thus a very close one. Spores are produced in the **sporangium** (plural, **sporangia**), the enlarged tip of the sporophyte. If they are carried to a moist surface, the spores germinate and form gametophytes. The mature gametophytes, in turn, produce eggs and sperm, either on separate plants or on separate branches. Rain or heavy dew carries the sperm from the male plant (or from the male branches of a male-female plant) to

Fig. 5.25   Life cycle of a moss. Compare this diagram with the schematic life cycle shown in Fig. 5.23.

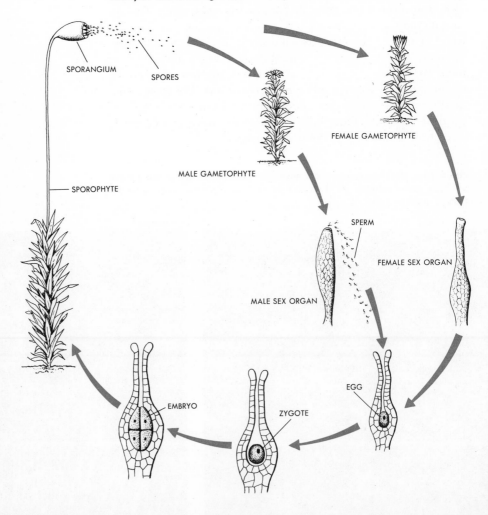

the several eggs produced by a gametophytic stalk. Fertilization takes place and several zygotes are produced at the tip of a female stalk, but, for some reason, only one survives and develops into a sporophyte.

The moss sporophyte achieves some degree of independence from the gametophyte through the development of chlorophyll, yet throughout its life it remains attached to the gametophyte. Thus it depends on the gametophyte for water, minerals, and perhaps more complex materials that regulate its growth and function. Even though the moss sporophyte is more independent of the gametophyte than is the case in liverworts, there is still a close physical relationship between the two.

The Ferns (Class FILICINEAE, Phylum TRACHEOPHYTA)

As a rule, the plants forming the groups you have studied so far are rather small. With few exceptions they are either aquatic or they are restricted to moist habitats. Both characteristics—small size and dependence on moist habitats—reflect a structural principle common to virtually all of them. Except for certain large brown algae, not one of the plants has specialized tissues for carrying water, minerals, and food throughout the body of the plant. As a result, these substances usually must diffuse slowly from one part of the plant to another. This inferior transportation system limits the size a plant can reach. Since aquatic forms are surrounded by water and dissolved minerals, the handicap is not as great as it is for land plants. This explains in part why certain algae grow to a large size.

The ferns (Fig. 5.26) are a major step upward in the plant kingdom. For the first time we meet plants with a transport system of specialized tissues that carry fluids throughout the plant body. These are called **vascular tissues,** and those plants that have them (ferns, fern-like plants, and seed plants) are called **vascular plants,** or **tracheophytes** (see Fig. 5.27). By virtue of their ability to transport water and minerals relatively long distances in a relatively short time, vascular plants are able to reach far greater sizes than nonvascular plants. Although the ferns most of us see do not attain great size, certain tropical tree ferns sometimes reach a height of 80 feet. Even the common ferns of the United States are much larger than mosses.

There are two types of vascular tissues **xylem** and **phloem** (Fig. 5.28), and each has a special function in plants. Xylem tissues carry water and dissolved minerals from the roots upward to other parts of the plant. Phloem transports soluble foods upward whenever the plant releases them from storage

Courtesy of The U.S. Forest Service

Fig. 5.26 Above: typical ferns growing on the forest floor (temperate zone). Below: tree ferns growing in Java.

W. H. Hodge

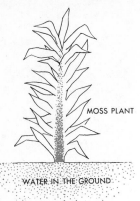

MOSS PLANT

WATER IN THE GROUND

TREE

WATER IN THE GROUND

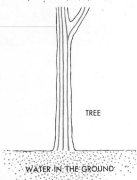

Fig. 5.27 Because nonvascular plants such as mosses have no specialized tissues for water conduction, there is a mechanical limit to the size they can reach. In contrast, vascular plants are frequently quite large.

Fig. 5.29 This drawing of a typical fern shows the plant in relation to the soil. Notice that the stem grows beneath the surface; only the leaves (fronds) are visible.

for use in the manufacture of new plant parts, and it transports newly-manufactured foods downward from the leaves. These tissues usually form a highly organized system that is spread throughout the roots, stems, and leaves. The system illustrated in Fig. 5.28 belongs to a typical young vascular plant, and as it matures, the system becomes more complex. Typically, the xylem and phloem tissues are grouped into **vascular bundles** in the stem (see drawing of cross section). If one of these bundles is magnified in longitudinal section, the xylem and phloem appear as slender tubes.

The typical fern is a plant whose leaves (called **fronds**) are often the only visible part. The stem and roots grow underground. In almost all species, the stem and roots survive for many years, while new leaves are produced each season. The fact that they grow year after year makes the ferns **perennial** plants. The fronds may project upward to a height of several feet. As they develop, they unroll in a curious fashion that makes a young leaf resemble the scroll of a violin. For this reason, developing fronds are sometimes called **fiddleheads.** In many species, the fronds are divided into **leaflets** that project outward from a central **rachis,** or axis. Fern structure is depicted in Fig. 5.29.

Fig. 5.28 A cross section of corn stem is shown below, highly magnified. Note the relative position and size of xylem and phloem tubes. The accompanying drawing shows how regions of vascular tissue fan out to all parts of a plant.

Courtesy Carolina Biological Supply House

PHLOEM TUBES

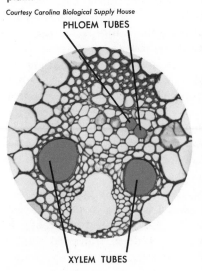

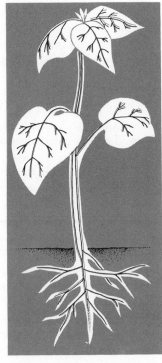

XYLEM TUBES

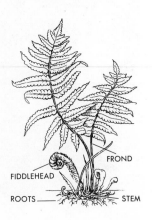

FROND

FIDDLEHEAD

ROOTS

STEM

Jean Carel

Courtesy Dr. H. C. Bold

Fig. 5.30 Above: the underside of a fern leaf, showing numerous *sori*, which are groups of sporangia (spore-producing structures). Right: a fern gametophyte, enlarged.

We have seen that in liverworts and mosses the gametophytic phase is more obvious than the sporophytic phase. The situation is reversed in ferns. The leafy part we see above ground is the sporophyte. The gametophyte is a small structure from which the sporophyte develops.

In the typical fern, spores are produced on specialized areas of the leaf, usually on the underside. The sporangia—spore cases—are produced in groups known as **sori** (singular, **sorus**). The sori (Fig. 5.30 left) are arranged in an orderly pattern on the fern leaf. When the plant is mature, the spores are released from their cases, fall to the ground, germinate, and develop into gametophytes. The gametophytes (Fig. 5.30 right) are flat, green structures that grow closely pressed to the soil. Seldom are they more than a quarter-inch in diameter. Gametophytes of most species of ferns are bisexual. Each gametophyte produces both sperm and eggs in specialized structures that develop on the under side, next to the soil. Usually, it takes several weeks from the time the spore germinates until the gametes reach maturity. Water from a rain or even a heavy dew enables the sperm to swim to the eggs. Although several eggs may be fertilized and form zygotes, only one zygote of a gametophyte succeeds in developing into a sporophyte. Once the zygote is formed, development is rapid. A root projects downward, and stem and leaf tissues form above the root. From this point on, growth and development produce the mature sporophyte, and thus complete the two-phase cycle (Fig. 5.31).

93

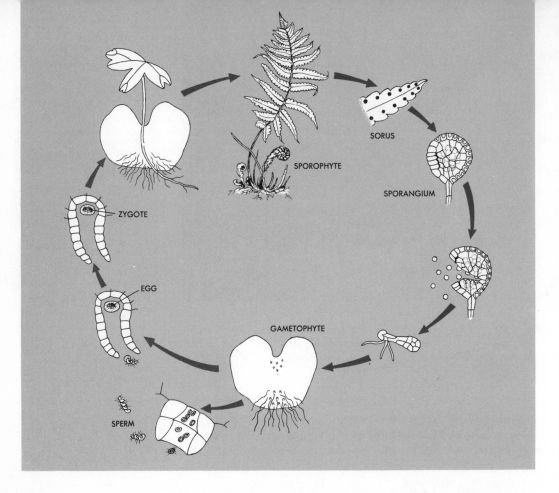

Fig. 5.31 Life cycle of a fern. Compare these stages with those of the schematic life cycle shown in Fig. 5.23. Where does meiosis occur in the fern life cycle? See the text for further clarification of this diagram.

Although some of the larger ferns are grown for ornamental purposes, the group is not of great economic importance to man, at least not the ferns that are alive today. About 300 million years ago, however, ferns and fern-like plants were the dominant vegetation on earth. During that time they formed the major basis for coal deposits, which have been of great economic importance to us.

The Seed Plants
(Classes GYMNOSPERMAE and ANGIOSPERMAE, Phylum TRACHEOPHYTA)

During the "Age of Ferns," some 300 million years ago, a new development in the reproductive structure of plants evolved. It has proved to be the most successful mechanism for the propagation of plants that nature has ever produced. That new development was the seed. It appeared first among the ferns. We have abundant fossil evidence of a group of extinct plants called **seed ferns.** It is interesting that modern ferns do not bear seeds; however, the seed plants form the most widely distributed and numerous plant group on Earth today. Apparently, this large and successful group of plants evolved from the seed ferns.

What is a seed, and why is it an especially efficient reproductive structure? The body of a seed plant, like that of a fern, is the sporophyte. The spores that it produces develop into gametophytes. However, the seed plant sporophyte produces two kinds of spores. One of these, the **microspore,** develops into a male gametophyte, while the **megaspore** gives rise to a female gametophyte. A seed plant's life cycle is shown in Fig. 5.32.

In seed plants, the gametophyte is even smaller than in ferns. The male gametophyte is simply the microspore (sometimes referred to as the **pollen grain**) and a tubular outgrowth containing several nuclei. The female gametophyte is only slightly more complex than this, and it remains imbedded within the tissues of the sporophyte throughout its functional existence. The female gametophyte develops within a structure called an **ovule,** which eventually matures and forms a seed. The ovule is composed of tissues specialized for the storage of food. Its outer cells form a protective layer. When the male gametophyte produces sperm, they reach the egg of the female through the pollen tube, and fertilization occurs. The zygote produces an immature, many-celled plant (the sporophyte), which reaches a limited stage of development. At this time, the stored food and protective tissues of the ovule surround the young sporophyte during a period of dormancy, or relative inactivity. In some species, the young sporophyte may take the storage materials into its tissues before dormancy.

A seed (Fig. 5.33), then, is a three-part reproductive structure. It has: 1. a young (embryonic) sporophyte, 2. stored food and protective tissue that the embryo will need when it begins to grow, and 3. outer tissues that surround and protect everything within.

Seeds may be rather small, such as seeds produced by mustard and carrot plants, and a variety of "weeds," or they may be quite large, as coconuts are. The size and construction of a seed are results of adaptation by natural selection. Small, light seeds are carried great distances by the wind. The coconut is adapted to float in water. Because the young sporophyte is protected from dryness, heat, cold, and other adverse conditions until conditions are favorable for growth, the species has an excellent chance of survival. Many seeds are so well constructed

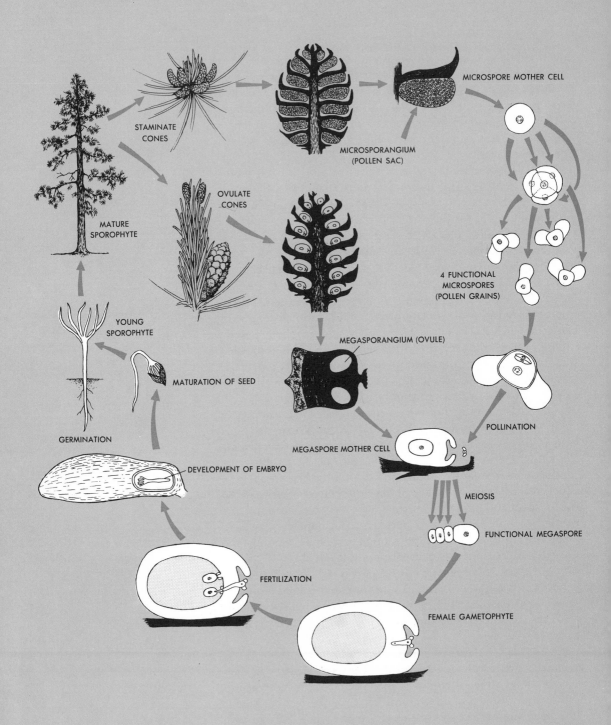

STAMINATE
CONES

MICROSPORE MOTHER CELL

MICROSPORANGIUM
(POLLEN SAC)

MATURE
SPOROPHYTE

OVULATE
CONES

4 FUNCTIONAL
MICROSPORES
(POLLEN GRAINS)

YOUNG
SPOROPHYTE

MEGASPORANGIUM (OVULE)

MATURATION OF SEED

POLLINATION

GERMINATION

MEGASPORE MOTHER CELL

DEVELOPMENT OF EMBRYO

MEIOSIS

FUNCTIONAL MEGASPORE

FERTILIZATION

FEMALE GAMETOPHYTE

Fig. 5.32 Life cycle of a pine tree: Although this life cycle appears complex, it is essentially the same kind of cycle you have been following since we discussed the liverworts.

that they can pass unharmed through the digestive systems of animals. Considering this superior reproductive device, it is not surprising that the vast majority of plant species and individual plants are seed plants (Table 5-1).

There are two clear-cut groups of seed plants—the **gymnosperms** (from the Greek words *gymnos,* naked, and *sperma,* seed) and the **angiosperms** (from the Greek word *angeion,* vessel). Among the gymnosperms are such familiar trees as pine, spruce, and fir, as well as many evergreen ornamental shrubs. The angiosperms include all flowering plants. The angiosperms are far more numerous than the gymnosperms. Of the approximately 250,000 known species of seed plants, fewer than 1,000 are gymnosperms.

Of the several types of gymnosperms, the **conifers,** cone-bearing trees, are by far the most outstanding (Fig. 5.34). Common evergreen trees and shrubs belong to this group. Pine, fir, and spruce are representative evergreen conifers. A few species, such as larch and cypress, are **deciduous,** meaning that all their leaves are shed at one season, instead of gradually, as in the case of evergreen leaves.

There are more than 500 known species of conifers, many of which are widely distributed. The great pine forests of the northern latitudes of the United States attest to the successful adaptation of this particular genus. Coniferous plants are of great economic importance to man. Many of them are sources of lumber and other products. The pine tree, for example,

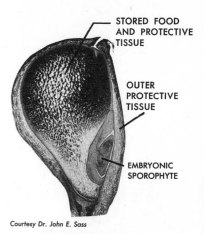

Courtesy Dr. John E. Sass

Fig. 5.33 Section of a corn seed, showing its three general areas.

Fig. 5.34 Stem tip of pine showing staminate cones. The needle-shaped leaves are characteristic of pines and many other conifers.

Courtesy of The American Museum of Natural History

Fig. 5.35 *Zamia floridana,* a cycad. Can you see why these plants are often called "palms?"

Julia Morton

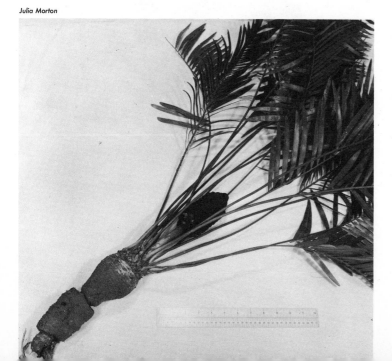

Fig. 5.36   With so many species of flowering plants, there is great diversity of floral structure. The three types shown here are representative of the larger flowers. Top: oriental poppy. Middle: cactus flower. Bottom: day lily.

Courtesy of The American Museum of Natural History

Lynwood M. Chace

Leonard Lee Rue III

produces not only valuable lumber but wood pulp, turpentine, and various resins. In addition, conifers are widely grown and sold by nurserymen as ornamental shrubs or trees.

Palm-like trees called **cycads** form another group of gymnosperms, particularly numerous in the tropics. The cycads (see Fig. 5.35) are plants with thick, fleshy stems which, if above ground, are armored with leaf bases, bearing a crown of large fern- or palm-like leaves. For this reason, they are sometimes confused with ferns and palms, which are not gymnosperms. Only one genus of cycad (*Zamia*) is native to the United States, and it is restricted to Florida. However, several other cycads are widely grown indoors as ornamental plants, and outdoors in subtropical and tropical climates.

There are more angiosperms—flowering plants—than all other plants combined (Fig. 5.36). The reason for this seems obvious. The flower is a highly efficient device for producing seeds. Essentially, a flower is a group of modified leaves that have specialized for various functions, including the production of spores. The typical flower exhibits four types of modified leaves: **sepals, petals, pistils** and **stamens,** as shown in Fig. 5.37.

While the stamen bears microspores (pollen grains), the pistil bears one or more ovules in the **ovary,** which is the lower portion of the pistil. Each ovule develops a megaspore within

Fig. 5.37   This generalized diagram of a complete flower shows the various floral parts. The ovary persists far longer than the others, and it develops into the fruit.

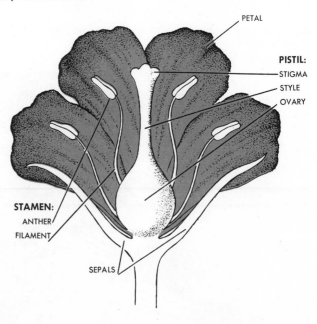

PETAL

PISTIL:
STIGMA
STYLE
OVARY

STAMEN:
ANTHER
FILAMENT

SEPALS

its tissues. The pistil and stamen are called the **essential** parts of the flower. Because the sepals and petals play no direct role in reproduction, they are called **accessory** parts. A flower that has these four parts is called a **complete** flower.

Although most angiosperms bear complete flowers, there are some species that do not. Grasses, for example, bear flowers that are generally without definite sepals and petals. Other plants bear flowers that have either stamens or pistils, but not both. Corn (Fig. 5.38), for example, has staminate flowers on the "tassel," and the pistillate flowers on the "ear." Still other species, such as the pussy willow and mulberry, have staminate and pistillate flowers on separate plants. Sometimes these are called "male" and "female" plants, but since the plant bodies are sporophytes, some botanists take issue with the "male" and "female" designations.

Even though the flowers of various angiosperms differ widely, all species reproduce sexually in a similar way. When the microspores (pollen grains) are produced by stamens, they are carried to pistils by a process called **pollination.** A variety of agents may be the pollinators—man, wind, water, insects. When pollen is carried from a flower of one plant to a flower of another plant belonging to the same species, the process is called **cross-pollination.** However, some flowers are self-pollinated.

Fig. 5.38   An experimental field of corn. The small staminate flowers are located on the "tassel," or terminal portion of the stalk, and the small pistillate flowers are on the "ear."

Courtesy Allied Chemical Corporation

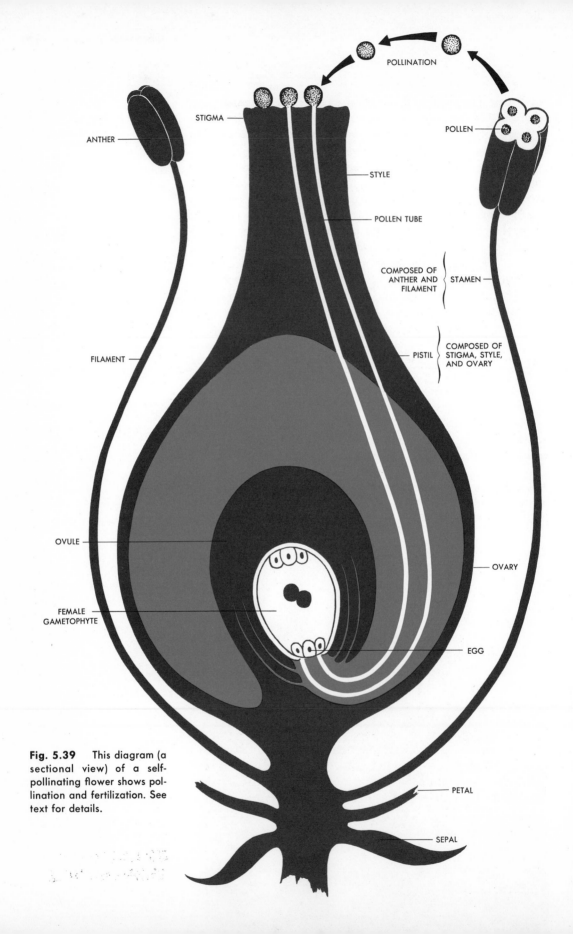

Fig. 5.39 This diagram (a sectional view) of a self-pollinating flower shows pollination and fertilization. See text for details.

In such plants the pollen transfer may take place by direct contact of a stamen with a pistil. In each situation, the pollen grain (microspore) nucleus divides and forms two nuclei. One of these two then divides, giving each pollen grain a total of three nuclei. This may take place before the pollen grain leaves the stamen, or it may be completed later. When a pollen grain reaches a particular part of the pistil (the **stigma**), it germinates and forms a **pollen tube.** One of the three nuclei is typically associated with growth of the tube and is called the **tube nucleus.** The other two, which will function as gametes, are called **sperm nuclei.** Note the diagram in Fig. 5.39.

One of the cells that lies deeply within the tissues of the developing ovule specializes as the megaspore and begins development into the female gametophyte. In most angiosperms, the megaspore nucleus undergoes three successive divisions and produces eight haploid nuclei, six of which become surrounded by cell walls. One of these six develops into an egg cell. The other five play no important part in the further development of the ovule. The two remaining nuclei are called **polar nuclei,** and they occupy a common cytoplasm. The mature female gametophyte, then, consists of seven cells, one of which has two nuclei.

By this time, a pollen tube has grown to the ovule, discharging its two sperm nuclei into the female gametophyte. One of these unites with the egg and forms a zygote. The other one joins the two polar nuclei (which may unite with each other first) and forms the **endosperm nucleus.** This, together with the surrounding cytoplasm develops into storage tissue (endosperm). The zygote develops into the embryonic sporophyte. When the embryo, endosperm, and outer coverings of the ovule have completed their development, the seed is ready to be released from the plant.

While the ovules are maturing into seeds, the ovary undergoes further development, forming the **fruit.** This may be a fleshy structure, as in the case of a tomato or watermelon, or it may be merely a dry pod, as in the case of bean, mustard, and many wild plants. Regardless of the many differences in details that exist in seed and fruit development, the seeds of flowering plants are *always* produced within a floral ovary. It is this characteristic that gives rise to the term "angiosperm." Gymnosperms do not bear flowers or fruits, and their seeds are borne *upon* modified leaves rather than *within* an enclosure such as the floral ovary. Apparently, the fruit is a highly successful adaptation resulting in wide distribution of the seeds of flowering plants. The flower-seed-fruit mechanism of reproduction goes far in explaining why the flowering plants are the dominant vegetation on the Earth.

CARL A. RUDISILL LIBRARY
LENOIR-RHYNE COLLEGE

SOME PLANTS AND ANIMALS THROUGH THE AGES

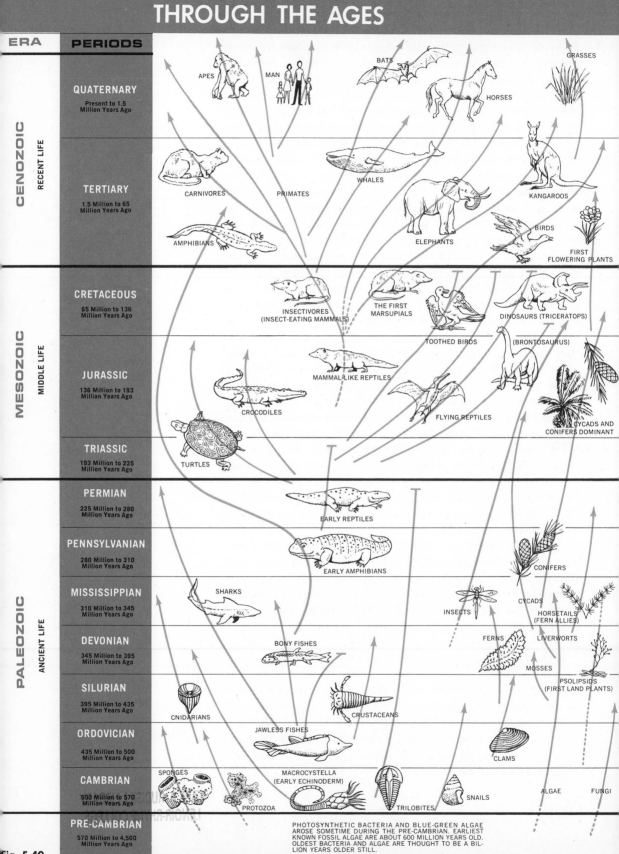

ERA	PERIODS	
CENOZOIC RECENT LIFE	**QUATERNARY** Present to 1.5 Million Years Ago	APES, MAN, BATS, HORSES, GRASSES
	TERTIARY 1.5 Million to 65 Million Years Ago	CARNIVORES, PRIMATES, WHALES, ELEPHANTS, KANGAROOS, BIRDS, FIRST FLOWERING PLANTS, AMPHIBIANS
MESOZOIC MIDDLE LIFE	**CRETACEOUS** 65 Million to 136 Million Years Ago	INSECTIVORES (INSECT-EATING MAMMALS), THE FIRST MARSUPIALS, TOOTHED BIRDS, DINOSAURS (TRICERATOPS), (BRONTOSAURUS)
	JURASSIC 136 Million to 193 Million Years Ago	CROCODILES, MAMMAL-LIKE REPTILES, FLYING REPTILES, CYCADS AND CONIFERS DOMINANT
	TRIASSIC 193 Million to 225 Million Years Ago	TURTLES
PALEOZOIC ANCIENT LIFE	**PERMIAN** 225 Million to 280 Million Years Ago	EARLY REPTILES
	PENNSYLVANIAN 280 Million to 310 Million Years Ago	EARLY AMPHIBIANS, CONIFERS
	MISSISSIPPIAN 310 Million to 345 Million Years Ago	SHARKS, INSECTS, CYCADS, HORSETAILS (FERN ALLIES)
	DEVONIAN 345 Million to 395 Million Years Ago	BONY FISHES, FERNS, LIVERWORTS, MOSSES
	SILURIAN 395 Million to 435 Million Years Ago	CNIDARIANS, CRUSTACEANS, PSOLIPSIDS (FIRST LAND PLANTS)
	ORDOVICIAN 435 Million to 500 Million Years Ago	JAWLESS FISHES, CLAMS
	CAMBRIAN 500 Million to 570 Million Years Ago	SPONGES, MACROCYSTELLA (EARLY ECHINODERM), PROTOZOA, TRILOBITES, SNAILS, ALGAE, FUNGI
	PRE-CAMBRIAN 570 Million to 4,500 Million Years Ago	PHOTOSYNTHETIC BACTERIA AND BLUE-GREEN ALGAE AROSE SOMETIME DURING THE PRE-CAMBRIAN. EARLIEST KNOWN FOSSIL ALGAE ARE ABOUT 600 MILLION YEARS OLD. OLDEST BACTERIA AND ALGAE ARE THOUGHT TO BE A BILLION YEARS OLDER STILL.

Fig. 5.40

Flowering plants have far more economic importance than all other plants combined. Among the flowering plants, the large deciduous trees, such as oak and hickory, are a source of wood for lumber and for a great variety of wood products. The textile industry uses the fibers of cotton and other flowering plants for the weaving of cloth. Still other flowering plants are valuable as sources of drugs or oils. Cereal grains, such as corn, wheat, and rice have been cultivated by man for thousands of years. Many other plants have been developed for their fruits— for example, apples, bananas, the citrus fruits, tomatoes, grapes, melons, and many common garden "vegetables" such as squash (the edible part of which is really a fruit, since it is a matured ovary of a flower). The roots of many plants, such as carrots, beets, and sweet potatoes, are also an important food source. Still others of this group are grown for their stems—the Irish potato (the "potato" is a modified stem, not a root), asparagus, and sugar cane. This list is hardly a complete one, but it serves to remind us of the extent to which we depend on the flowering plants every day.

The Evolution of Plants

When we study evolution, we must use the approach of the historian. First, we must gather evidence. When it is inconclusive, then we must do the best we can to reconstruct events. In plant evolution, the major sources of evidence are the fossil record, comparative morphology, biochemistry, cytogenetics, and geographical distribution of the plants now living.

In spite of the abundance of data that we have from these fields of study, there are large gaps in our knowledge of plant evolution. One of the major difficulties is that many of the smaller plants did not lend themselves well to fossilization. But even if the fossil record were complete, it would not necessarily tell us any more about the **origins** of specific plant groups than we now know. Any account of plant evolution has to be based to a certain extent on some intelligent guesswork. The modern biologist is in the position of a detective who is faced with the obvious fact that a safe has been blown open and yet may never find out exactly how it was done.

Many botanists believe that the first living organisms were heterotrophs, not unlike modern bacteria, and that photosynthetic bacteria and the blue-green algae developed very early from these organisms. This view is upheld by the fact that the earliest known fossil plants (about 600 million years old) are those of simple algae that are much like modern blue-green algae. Also, there is indirect evidence that both algae and bacteria had existed for nearly a billion years before that time (see the time chart in Fig. 5.40).

The origins of the fungi are rather obscure, but they probably arose from the algae rather than from original heterotrophic cells such as bacteria. There is strong evidence that land plants evolved from green algae perhaps 500 million years ago, after which there was great diversification. But the exact origins of the different groups are obscure, and the evidence can be interpreted in different ways. Vascular, fern-like plants are among the earliest land plants known; fossil mosses and liverworts appear in later fossil deposits, which may mean that they evolved more recently than did vascular plants.

Ferns and fern-like plants, some of which were gigantic, made up the major vegetation of the Earth until some 150 million years ago. At that time the cycads and conifers became dominant. The earliest known fossil angiosperms are at least 125 million years old. Within a few million years they had succeeded in replacing gymnosperms as the major plants. This trend has continued to the present time, with the result that the vast majority of modern plants are angiosperms. Figure 5.40 shows something of these general evolutionary trends and relates the plants to the animals in their evolution.

SUMMARY

We have presented the plant kingdom in seven groups of plants—algae, fungi, lichens, liverworts, mosses, ferns, and seed plants. Although certain other plant types are known, these seven groups represent the plants we most commonly see.

Of the approximately 350,000 known species of plants, about 250,000 are flowering plants. This indicates the successful adaptation of this group.

In their reproductive habits, the vast majority of plants produce spores by a process of meiosis, and these spores give rise to haploid plants. The union of gametes produces the sporophyte, thus completing a cycle that shows alternation of two generations—the gametophyte and the sporophyte. Seed plants, and particularly flowering plants, have reproductive structures that are highly complex and specialized.

The algae probably evolved from ancestral forms at least a billion years ago. Land plants evidently arose from the algae about 500 million years ago. Since that time, ferns and fern-like plants, gymnosperms, and angiosperms have succeeded each other in that order as the dominant plants on Earth.

FOR THOUGHT AND DISCUSSION

1 What good are algae?

2 A student once wrote on a test, "Bacteria are very bad. They cause diseases and eat up the good plants and animals." Evaluate this statement. Can we really speak of organisms as "bad" and "good"? Assuming that we can call some bacteria "bad," or, perhaps, harmful to man's interests, does this apply to all bacteria? Incidentally, do bacteria "eat?"

3 Generally speaking, vascular plants reach much larger size than nonvascular plants. How do you account for this?

4 Why do we consider the lichens to be a major plant group, and yet they are not given their own phylum in Table 5-1?

5 Distinguish between sexual and asexual reproduction.

6 Distinguish between a fruit and a vegetable.

7 The cells of endosperm tissue in most flowering plants are triploid (3n). How do the cells of this tissue come to have this particular chromosomal constitution?

SELECTED READINGS

Bold, H. C. *Morphology of Plants*. New York: Harper and Brothers, 1957.
Bold gives an exhaustive and authoritative presentation of the world of plants.

————— *The Plant Kingdom* (2nd ed.). Englewood Cliffs, N.J.: Prentice-Hall, Inc., 1964.
The author of the rather comprehensive book cited above surveys the plant kingdom in this small volume.

Cronquist, A. *Introductory Botany*. New York: Harper and Brothers, 1960.
This is one of several excellent textbooks of general botany. It is mentioned especially because it presents the plant kingdom in an evolutionary perspective.

Schery, R. W. *Plants for Man*. Englewood Cliffs, N.J.: Prentice-Hall, Inc., 1952.
The viewpoint of this book is the economic importance of various plants.

6 DIVERSITY, SIMILARITY, AND THE HUMAN VIEWPOINT

In the introductory chapters we said that certain principles govern the world of living things. We did not say that those principles apply to only one kingdom of organisms and not to the other. If you have followed the arguments in this book carefully, you should now be able to talk quite specifically about similarities *and* differences that exist between plants and animals (see Fig. 6.1). You should also be able to describe diversity among the various categories of animals and the various categories of plants as you move upward or downward among the phyla.

In describing diversity, we have not meant to establish a hard-and-fast cleavage between plants and animals. To do so would destroy the concepts of basic similarities among all organisms. In this concluding chapter we shall attempt to show something of the similarities that exist in the very presence of diversity.

Courtesy of The American Museum of Natural History

Courtesy of The American Museum of Natural History

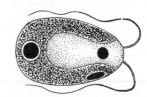

Fig. 6.1 What are the *basic* similarities between an elephant and a maple tree? What are their *basic* differences? What biological characteristics does *Chlamydomonas* share with each?

Order in Diversity

In the 1800's, when descriptive biology was making its greatest gains, major emphasis was placed on differences existing among organisms. Actually, this period of activity extended well back into the 1700's, before Linnaeus began his work, and continued into the 1900's. While there is still a need for this viewpoint in biological research, the emphasis of modern biology on cellular and molecular aspects of life is revealing striking similarities among organisms. These similarities help us to see order in diversity and, by so doing, enable us to view the world of living things as a meaningful whole.

Let us consider a few examples. So far as we know, all organisms (except for certain viruses, if these are to be considered organisms) have within their cells control systems consisting of the substance DNA. As we have seen, this substance has remarkable properties. For one, it is self-duplicating. For another, DNA molecules control the formation of new protein molecules. These, in turn, dictate exactly how much and what kind of new materials will be built within the cell. If the organism in which this occurs is very complex, as in a human being or a tree, the ultimate shape, size, color, and texture of mature parts will be dictated indirectly by cellular DNA. It seems incredible that so much in nature is dependent upon so little; also, that in spite of the differences between a man and an oak tree, each develops from a cell whose nucleus contains a substance very much like that contained by the other.

The cellular metabolism of all organisms is remarkably similar. For example, water is the common solvent of all living matter; it makes up about two-thirds of the mass of virtually all cells. The relative proportions of the fuel substances (carbohydrate and fat) and of the structural and enzymatic material (protein) are about the same in most cells, no matter where they are found. The same is true of vitamins and minerals. Many of the enzyme systems in cells of organisms quite low on the evolutionary scale are also found in the cells of organisms which are only distantly related to them. What does this mean? It is a reflection of at least some basic genetic similarities. Enzyme (protein) molecules are formed as a result of "instructions" that are "dictated" by genes. Certain genes, then, are apparently widespread in genetic systems.

Finally, to conclude this brief list of similarities in cell metabolism, organic molecules are broken down for their potential energy in much the same way by all organisms. Certain compounds within cells function in the transformation of this energy to a more readily expendable form. These compounds are found in all living matter.

Mechanisms of reproduction are also very similar among all organisms. Although certain differences exist, the basic processes are very much the same. Remember that reproduction occurs at **molecular, cellular,** and **organismal** levels. We have already mentioned that only the nucleic acids are capable of reproduction at the molecular level, and that this process is characteristic of all cells. At the cellular level, cell division is the reproductive process. There are some cells of *all species* that have the ability to divide and thus produce daughter cells that have an equal distribution of vital materials.

At the organismal level, there are many differences in reproductive processes, but these differences are simply variations of either asexual or sexual reproduction. There are very few basic types of asexual reproduction—the body of an animal may divide in some fashion and form two or more individuals; a plant may produce special cells or clusters of cells called spores, or a part of its body may develop into a complete individual. The essence of sexual reproduction is the union of two specialized gametes which form a zygote. The zygote then develops into a new organism. This phenomenon is widespread in both the plant and the animal kingdoms. Finally, the process of meiosis, described in an earlier chapter, is a remarkably similar process wherever it occurs.

These few examples of fundamental similarity among organisms point up the common origin of organisms from primitive life forms existing many millions of years ago. In the long processes of adaptation and natural selection, many of these molecular and cellular characteristics have remained virtually unchanged ever since the great proliferation of species began. If life began some two billion years ago, and evidence indicates that it did, then evolutionary history divides itself into two time periods of roughly equal length.

During the first period, the cell established itself as the basic unit of life. It was during this time that the characteristics we have just discussed, and others, developed as a result of natural selection. The cells that were able to evolve these mechanisms were the "fittest," survived, and played a further role in evolution. During the second period, natural selection moved to a new level. It gave rise to diversity at the organism level, that is, diversity of external form. But the most efficient mechanisms were already firmly established at the molecular and cellular levels, and they have persisted to the present time.

The vast array of organisms around us today are all closely interrelated. To study them as a whole, we must adopt the viewpoint of the ecologist. The complicated food webs are but one example of the many relationships between plants and animals. In the water, algae and other small plants are the producers, both of energy-yielding organic molecules and oxygen, while land plants serve this function in terrestrial environments. Fungi and other decomposers provide the mineral substances for these producers, while various animals consume plants and each other. At the same time these animals and the decomposers produce carbon dioxide and other materials that are useful in the metabolism of the producers.

In addition to these nutritional relationships, there are those which have to do with maintaining the temperature, light, and moisture needs of various species. For example, most animals depend on a plant habitat in which they can live and reproduce successfully. Various plants have a characteristic fauna associated with them; remove the plants, and the animals also disappear. Finally, there are such relationships as parasitism and mutualism through which plants and animals are associated. These examples point up the fact that we cannot dissect nature into species and kingdoms without distorting it to some degree. The great web of nature is an endless series of relationships among all organisms inhabiting the Earth.

Man's Place in Nature

As the oak tree and the variety of animals that live among its branches and that burrow among its roots are a part of nature, so is man. Considering the long line of success of other species, man is a relatively recent arrival on Earth, yet the place he has made for himself, as a species, has been unparalleled in the great succession of life. As they have in the past, his fortunes depend largely on the wisdom with which he exploits his environment.

Unfortunately, man tends to be enormously wasteful of natural resources, both living and nonliving (Fig. 6.2). It is only within recent decades that much organized effort—conservation programs—has been made to curb this wastefulness. As a result, wanton destruction of natural resources has been reduced somewhat. However, more effective conservation measures are still needed at the national and international levels. In addition, many of the laws governing the use of natural resources were passed when certain aspects of conservation were poorly understood; consequently, they need revision. This is particularly true of laws concerning game and fish. Many laws are not reasonable in the light of recent ecological findings, but it is difficult for wildlife biologists to have them changed as rapidly as our knowledge advances.

We have been more successful with conservation of plant

Courtesy Rhodesia National Tourist Office

Fig. 6.2 When man alters the face of the earth, plant and animal life are usually affected. The photograph above shows the plight of displaced animals during the building of a reservoir in Rhodesia. In some such cases, game rescue operations, as shown in the photograph below, were effective.

Courtesy Rhodesia National Tourist Office

resources than we have with animals (Fig. 6.3). For example, many years ago it became apparent that our forests were being depleted. Such safeguards as selective cutting of timber, reseeding, and the prevention of forest fires helped enormously. In general, these measures are our best defense against forest depletion.

One of the greatest problems in conservation is the constant danger of upsetting what is often called the "balance of nature." For example, an area may be sprayed with insecticide to kill an insect pest. In killing the insects, however, its natural enemies may also be killed, including other insects and birds. Quite frequently, spraying brings about a situation worse than the situation it was intended to cure, or relief may be only temporary. This upset of "balance" sometimes has such far reaching effects that a farmer's crops, or even his domesticated animals, are harmed. Ranchers of the western United States once conducted an intensive campaign against coyotes, which were killing livestock. The ranchers' efforts were quite successful, but with the decline of the coyote population, rabbits began to overrun the country. The rabbits were more than a mere nuisance because they ate vegetation that the livestock needed. When people realized that the coyotes were necessary to keep the rabbits in check, the ranchers began to consider the coyotes the lesser of two evils and relaxed their efforts.

Fig. 6.3   Man's influence over nature is not always destructive. At left conservationists make a study of a pine forest in British Honduras. At right a fish ladder at Bonneville Dam makes it possible for salmon to swim past the dam to spawn. Through the institution of such conservation measures, our natural resources can be preserved.

Courtesy The United Nations   *Courtesy U.S. Department of the Interior, Fish and Wildlife Service*

Man's relation to nature, however, reaches beyond those organisms that are useful or harmful to him. What of man's relation to man? Aside from political, social, and ethical considerations, which are beyond the scope of this book, two outstanding dangers exist. The first is **pollution** (Fig. 6.4), the accumulation of waste materials. The body wastes of man are not the major problem, but even so, they sometimes spread disease which kills plants and animals. Every large city has its sewage problems, especially where there are rivers or harbors. Industrial wastes, insecticide residues, and a variety of such products enter the air, water, and soil. They remain there, or are deposited elsewhere, and damage plants and animal life, and man himself. Also, there are radioactive wastes from industrial and military operations. It is extremely difficult to dispose of them, and possibly they constitute a greater long-range threat to man than nuclear warfare.

The second danger, and one that compounds the pollution problem, is **overpopulation** (note Fig. 6.5). We are now seeing a "population explosion" in the world. Within the past century the population of the world has more than doubled, and with longer life expectancies and lower mortality rates among infants, it is climbing at an alarming rate. Just how long this trend can continue is difficult to say, but it is a problem that demands the attention of all of us. It is not simply a matter of food. It is more a problem of pollution and of sheer living space. Of all of the social and biological problems facing modern man, the world population problem is the greatest, if not the most urgent.

Courtesy Wisconsin Conservation Department

Fig. 6.4 These fish were killed by pollution that was allowed to enter their waters. With increased human populations, it is becoming more difficult to control the pollution of water, soil, and air.

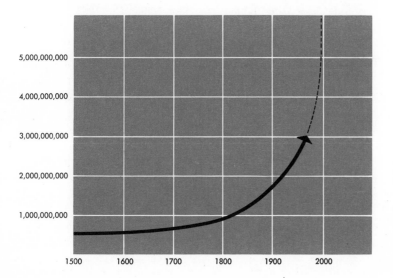

Fig. 6.5 World population figures and rate of increase are shown since the year 1500. The dotted line represents a projection of human population increase based on past and present trends. You might ponder Question 4 at the end of this chapter in the light of this chart.

FOR THOUGHT AND DISCUSSION

1 Do plant and animal kingdoms actually exist in nature? If you feel that this question might logically be answered by either yes or no, defend each answer.

2 In external form and function, a human being and an oak tree would seem to have little, if anything, in common. What basic similarities can you list between them?

3 What do we mean by "upsetting the balance of nature?" Is there really a "balance" in nature?

4 At the present rate of increase in the human population, it has been estimated that there will be one human being per square yard of Earth's land surface by the year 2500! Obviously, something will be done to alter the rate of increase before such a population is reached. What do you think this "something" will be?

SELECTED READINGS

Bates, M. *Man In Nature* (2nd ed.). Englewood Cliffs, N.J.: Prentice-Hall, Inc., 1964.

A distinguished student of human biology considers man's relationship to his surroundings.

Bonner, J. T. *The Ideas of Biology.* New York: Harper and Brothers, 1962.

This excellent short book is a synthesis of broad principles of biology. Although the book is well worth reading in its entirety, Chapter 5 is of special interest. It is entitled "Simple to Complex," and discusses certain issues closely related to the first part of Chapter 6 of this book.

Carson, R. *Silent Spring.* Boston: Houghton Mifflin Co., 1962.

The author of this book urges caution in our attempts to control nature, and presents an excellent picture of ecological relationships.

Thomas, W. L., Jr. (ed.). *Man's Role In Changing the Face of the Earth.* Chicago: University of Chicago Press, 1956.

An informative presentation of man's various activities in exploiting nature.

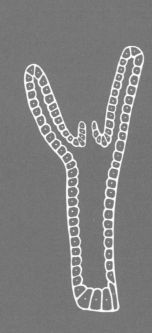 **INDEX**